Glyn Edwards was des
of the 'most exciting yc
gave him the first oppo
His first collection wil
Lonely Press. He is a te

Rose Widlake was the inaugural winner of the Terry Hetherington Young Writers Award in 2009, and became a trustee of the award in 2015. In the past she has worked for Parthian Books and Candy Jar Books, and she currently works for Southbank Centre as a fundraiser. She lives in London.

Also available

Cheval 10
Cheval 9
Cheval 8
Cheval 7
Cheval 6
Cheval 5
Cheval 4
Cheval 3
Cheval 2
Cheval

Cheval 11

Edited by Glyn Edwards and Rose Widlake

Foreword by Aida Birch

Parthian, Cardigan, SA43 1ED
www.parthianbooks.com
ISBN 978-1-912681-08-2
First published in 2018 © the contributors
Edited by Rose Widlake and Glyn Edwards
Cover Design by Rose Horridge
Typeset by Alison Evans
Printed and bound by Pulsio

Contents

Foreword

The Terry Hetherington Young Writers Award is in the namesake of the late poet Terry Hetherington, who died in 2007. His poetry collection, *The Undiminished*, published by Swansea Poetry Workshop, draws attention to his life. The collection reveals a deep love of words, of Wales, of history and culture. From the age of seven he was an avid reader – widely read, and later widely published. He was invariably wise, and he loved to share the joy of poetry and literature with young writers.

The Trustees of the Terry Hetherington Young Writers Award derive great pleasure from seeing the past winners become established writers, and having their own collections published. Some have been awarded further literary prizes; others have been invited to read at literature festivals at home and abroad. Some past prizewinners have benefited from exchange literature tours to India. Their success is ongoing as they continue to make their mark in the world of literature and poetry.

Cheval 11 is edited by Rose Widlake and Glyn Edwards. Both are past prizewinners of the Terry Hetherington Young Writers Award. The collection is published by Parthian Books, and the encouragement of Maria Zygogianni and Richard Davies has been most constructive.

We are most grateful to all those who entered the 2018 award. The entries have been of a very high standard, making it a difficult task for the judges.

The winning entry was 'The Silver Darlings', a story by Katya Johnson. The story was described by the judges as having a well-researched history. It holds the reader's interest throughout. Second Prize, Poetry, was awarded to Thomas Tyrrell for his poem 'Sometimes in Summer', noted as having a melodious sound and an eye for beauty. Michael Muia was awarded Second Prize, Fiction, for his story titled 'Young Tommy'. It is a very vivid story full of emotion. Thomas Baker was Highly Commended for his poem, 'The Barren Land', that combines the history and beauty of a Welsh Valley. Nathan Munday's distinctive story 'Tylluan' has a fascinating link to Welsh mythology and was awarded Commended.

All the contributors for the 2018 Terry Hetherington Young Writers Award have submitted both poetry and fiction of varied degrees of excellence. Their stories and poetry are compelling and profound. Many contributors send entries year after year. Their endurance and fortitude is very much appreciated. We are unable to publish all the entries for this year's award, but we hope to receive another entry from the contributors for the Terry Hetherington Young Writers Award 2019.

An added bonus this year has been the competition organised by Parthian Books to design the cover for *Cheval 11*. This inclusion is an innovative idea that adds visual charm to the anthology.

Aida Birch

Preface

A writer charges to their teens with a pen in hand, trying to score something permanent about the implausible self on the impossible earth. In diaries, journals, blogs, sketchbooks, this writer excavates channels of self-discovery me my I me my I. Gradually, painfully, they become so fluent in digging that they seek instead to build. Though, there being so little time to build and so, so many structures to ape, that a writer briefly forgets they are a writer, and fills their hands with books and bricks and baby's bottles. Soon, they forget why they wrote. Next, then they forget that they wrote. Then they forget.

The Terry Hetherington Prize was created to encourage writers to the realisation that, should they dig further and dig longer, should they take their time in prudent planning and blissful building, that there would be cityscapes for such structures to survive in.

Over a decade later, the trustees of the Prize under the careful dedication of Aida Birch have ensured that hundreds of writers, at an age when the noise of the world around could have muffled their prose or starched their verse can neither forget their craft, nor their potential for craft.

Cheval 11 is this year's architecture – the statue in its town centre, standing taller than his legacy, pen in hand, is the poet Terry Hetherington. This year's judging panel would urge you to visit 'The Silver Darlings' by Katya Johnson and Thomas Tyrell's 'Sometimes in Summer' and 'Young Tommy' by Michael Muia. In your second sitting, please enjoy the commended entries 'The Barren Land' by Thomas Baker and 'Tylluan' by Nathan Munday.

Within its walls, a reader may recognise new writing by previous winners and commended entrants of the Prize and will encounter on their travels previously unpublished work by some of the Wales' most promising young writers. The flags are raised, however, in particular celebration of those poets and authors who will encounter their work in print for the first time here. We hope the experience is monumental.

Enjoy your stay. Return often.

Glyn Edwards and Rose Widlake
Editors

Terry Hetherington

Movement

A dry stone wall crowns the hill
I lean on it, the cold
rock-lumps against my back
a frost-bound rippled field.
Before me steeply falls the hill,
then swells out gently, forms a mound,
drops again, shelves and slopes,
twists and bucks, always down
towards the town where slated
roofs run in rows,
on and on, straight and true,
twine and turn, rise and fall,
fly off at tangents,
slew and lean, climb and slide,
then to my side,
intruding movement – tangible,
a distant fox invades my eye,
one moment's blur, he makes the gorse.
I turn again, see a slope,
see the town:
All movement gone.

First published in *Over Milk Wood* (Alun Books), 2000

David Alun Williams

Cento, from The Undiminished

A tribute to the life of Terry Hetherington

In the peculiar pull of the bloodline
Steeped in Celtic lore
Heart and spirit shovelled out of ages past
Inked into the skin
As old as the earth.

Ah, you of nurtured life
Mind and body craving
His tune ecstasy and despair
Flotsam of bloodied tide of war
That opened the vein of his revolution.

Directing your gaze to the heavens
You have sought the scales of reasoning
In the flowering of a strange benevolence
Hoarding the remnants of a dream
To find him there.

I watched you weave the miracles of banter
With the ritual care
And feel the shuddering birth pangs of his hills
The pattern of conversation
No honeyed words could bribe.

Hearing the Merlin call
As you touch some life I do not see
Of the mystical voice flicks at my ear
As mute testimony to his existence
Wind stirred triumphant in the bracken.

You see hope, strength even
Clear and fluid
Burned years before
Like an extended ritual
Unfiltered by the guiding hand.

He drank? a mystery
Ah, the roar of the irony
The rising of alcohol sap
A periodic shedding of grace
Has the power of the multi-bladed.

And I dream now
The gift of your presence
Lighting up the room with your eyes
And I am hauled back through snarling time
In his enclosed link to earth.

From some abandoned holding
Oh, from the weathered walls of old
Your great gnarled hand contracted wrought fragility
Seeking reflections
Beyond the urban drift.

On memory's blurred face
With his visit nearing its end
Cocoon his somnolent body from the night
It is all long past
Time? Time is short.

I have come here, as the sea comes
To us, this estuary its wide peace
Where, drowsy in a soft inebriation
Our senses flow
Loaded with sunlit dreams, running from his mind.

I profile for past, for origins
Of the soul's primal rapture
for the coming of his art
This was his way
Here on the hill.

The field is an island of light
Sways the rhythm of a new tune
To tell us again
Of exhumed mystery
And mark the angle of parts.

Thomas Baker

The Barren Land

(Highly Commended)

'Guide me o thou Great Jehovah,
pilgrim through this barren land'
– 'Cwm Rhondda', William Williams Pantycelyn

My father used to bring me here for the view,
just as his father brought him.
The valley was much different
for them to what it is now – metal monstrosities whirred
and were dug in to the feet of the hills,
harvesting the dark marrow beneath the surface.
There were deep carbon wounds, symbolic
of a whipped and tirelessly worked landscape,
and noxious carbuncles that people genially labelled 'tips'—
much like this one reclaimed from the grey of history.
If you were to look north then south the horizons
were a congregation of languorous chimney smoke,
incoming acid rains and blade-sharp winds.
Between these ever encroaching horizons the terraces
tumbled, tilted and twisted in to one another,
clung precariously to the steep sides of impossible hills.
They're still there now – pebble dashed or brightly painted
to give the vague impression of a society in progress.
But going or gone are the men who once lived there
– teak tough men named Dai or Ivor with strapping muscles

and unslakable thirsts; men my father would
wax-lyrical about, the aristocrats of the opened earth.
I can imagine them now walking in an uneasy
unison to the pithead, swaggering with machismo,
thinking that they'll break the dark heart of this world.
Yet they have only found the silent spaces beneath,
the unending galleries propped up by death,
and so their world has taken its last wheezy breath.
Now I stand here today as an interrogator of what is left.
It is true, the air is now headier with the wild scent
of savage ferns and this day the blue sky blooms outwards,
and puffs of cloud trail towards the capital conferring
on it the status of a mid-distant fairytale kingdom
– the promised land of call centres and staid officialdom.
Once again I avert my eyes to the leafy valley below
and realise that this is how it has always been
– everything funnelling away to a supposedly better place;
the working pride, a sense of purpose, the dignity of industry
– all went down the railway line before that too went away.
That which remains, what nature or time has not reclaimed,
seems to now wither to the point of shabby obscurity.
Why then return to this place, this tumulus of an industry
where the sharp wind is a solemn hymn sung repeatedly?
Is it because I remember and am unable to forget?
Do I come here to connive with the mute ghosts of a past
and hope to find myself youthful again, bounding up
the rugged trail in the wake of my father's sure, steady gait,
looking down upon all my world as it seemed to be then
– endless terraces, thorny brambles, a mischievous Eden.
In the sullen waste of my heart I know that this cannot be done.
Yet I often return here as both pilgrim and prodigal son
to cut myself from the same stubborn generational seam,
give a manly handshake to the past and be gone.

Yalan Bao

China

My father seldom spoke to me
when he did, he mimicked the voice of my country
unwavering and unmoving, as if generated
from the hollow of the cosmos.
as he spoke, he would fix me with a vacant stare
reminding me of a slow-moving, sinuous river
from which I was afraid
that something menacing would emerge
to see through me and the ostentatious
shape I moulded myself into
which I wore like a garment
to please him and to win his approval
like the obedient daughter who was too mindful
of her self-image
to feel the disintegration within her
My country seldom spoke to me
when she did, she stole the voice of my father.

Kathy Chamberlain

Mr Goodwin

We used to go to him on Sundays. He would sit in his huge green armchair and stare at us, his eyes a sharp, pale blue amongst the mass of wrinkles. Mr Goodwin.

We usually had a fight before we went, because he was mean and ungrateful and Robbie didn't like wearing ties. I hated wearing dresses, but that didn't seem to matter. Somehow I would find myself, in giant puffball skirt with matching ribbons in my straggly hair, perched carefully on the edge of his worn leather settee.

Hands in our laps, we knew better than to fiddle or, God forbid, touch anything. Robbie had picked up a photo frame once. Silver, with a laughing brunette – her long, glossy curls tumbling down delicate shoulders. A tall, smiling man stood next to her, eyes fixed on her face. Robbie stared at the picture.

'Mr Goodwin, is that—'

It might have been the only time we ever saw Mr Goodwin get out of his chair. He snatched the frame from Robbie's hands, then slowed his movements, to place it gently back on the mantelpiece.

Mum gave us a talk later that evening, frizzy brown curls batting against her pink cheeks as her gaze flicked between the two of us. She stood with her hands on her wide hips.

'It's not our business. You mustn't pry, you'll upset him.'

I felt the remorse more keenly than Robbie. I think I always did. Dad called me sensitive. Mum had other, less kind, words for it.

Mr Goodwin had a plethora of unkind words for the world. He seemed against manners, never saying thank you for the weekly gift one of us would hesitantly bring. Usually it was fruit. Mr Goodwin would set it aside and ignore it. I often wondered if he ate any of it. I imagined the tall, locked cupboard under the stairs to contain a mountain of mouldy apples, nectarines and grapes.

It appeared to me that adults didn't eat fruit. Rather, they encouraged – demanded – that we eat our bitter apple and brown banana a day, but at a certain point in life they just stopped trying and lived instead on mashed potato and sherry. Mr Goodwin told Mum to cut out the drink when we popped round on Christmas Eve. He said it made her look like a chubby tart. Mum looked at the floor. Dad had no reply.

We usually had no reply for Mr Goodwin. 'Bite your tongue.' That was Dad's sage advice. It didn't matter what he said. That we shouldn't bother coming over, that I looked underfed, that he suspected Robbie was 'more than a little slow.' We battled through with prosaic pleasantries and small talk. Occasionally Mum would pay him a compliment and he would look down at his bulging stomach, almost crestfallen. I never understood why she was nice to him.

I didn't have many old people to compare him with. Three of my grandparents had died before I was born. Only my dad's mum, Granny, had stuck it out. She was a sweet, gentle little lady who lived by the sea, a two hour drive away. When we visited she made scones with currants in. Robbie and I surreptitiously removed them and stuffed them in our pockets, to be dropped out of the car windows on the way home. Mum would make the tea and listen to Granny's complaints about her neighbours and when they put the bins out. Dad would ask if she had any jobs that needed doing and go out to the shed to get the tools, all smiles.

He never smiled when Mum nudged him towards Mr Goodwin's shed. It was almost hidden at the back of the garden, behind low-hanging branches, under a crown of thick green leaves. The wooden-panelled walls were shrouded in cobwebs and grime. Dad used to swear sometimes, under his breath, when he put the key in the lock and some of the muck coated his hands. We offered to go with him in case he needed help, just to get out of the gloomy living room for a few minutes.

Despite Mr Goodwin's permanent upstairs presence, we actually spent some rather fun summer days in that garden. Weeding turned into a lesson in making daisy chains. Robbie promised to show me how, on condition I told no one at school.

He held a stem out for me to inspect. 'Press gently – just here – see? – with the tip of your nail.'

I was in awe of him as he casually made the central incision and threaded another stem through it. Once I'd mastered that, he went and kicked the football around the garden for a good half an hour.

We learnt how to get the neighbour's cat to come on to the lawn, with the help of an old dog bowl and a little milk. We called him Garfield because of his ginger fur and tickled his stomach when he rolled over to stretch.

July was suddenly August. My pasty legs caught the sun and Robbie and I set up a shop with some odds and ends from the shed and a handful of old coins we found in a jar. When it was time to leave Mum would call us in and we'd go to say goodbye to Mr Goodwin. Mum kissed him on the cheek and we took it in turns to gingerly place a kiss to the top of his bent head while he muttered and told us not to feel the need to call in the next week.

We always did. In all the years we stopped by I never once saw any other visitors. I asked Mum one time, when she was dragging the brush through my hair to get it into a ponytail fit for a visit, where Mr Goodwin's family were. She kept brushing for at least a minute, her eyes not meeting mine in the mirror. When she put the brush down she ran a finger along my cheek and turned me to face her.

'Mr Goodwin doesn't have any family.'

A frown marred her usually serene features. I didn't have a response to that, so I nodded. And didn't bring it up again.

As with church, I got to the age when I tried to put my foot down about going. While they conceded to my dropping out of Sunday School, my parents insisted I accompany them to see Mr Goodwin. He'd always seemed like an old man to me, but now he was frail, too. One small shiver and Mum would cover him with a thick fleece blanket. He no longer raised his arms to try to push her away. And he stopped telling us not to visit.

The outside world began to impinge on my time. I accepted my mother's insistence that I miss hours shopping with my school friends, but maintained that I needed to bring homework with me. It passed the time. One day, my head bent over a particularly vexing simultaneous equation, Mr Goodwin asked me a question about the sums. My mouth hung open before he waved a hand and went back to looking out of the window. I felt foolish, as though I'd missed an opportunity. It was the first time he tried to initiate conversation, but it wouldn't be the last.

The next week, Robbie was home, visiting from uni for the weekend. Mr Goodwin grabbed the armrests on either side of his chair and pushed himself a little more upright.

'So, boy. How are you finding university then?'

I kept my gaze fixed on my history assignment, but listened in awe as Robbie filled him in on his course, casual as anything. Robbie went on to tell him about a prank one of the boys he lived with had played on him and my eyes snapped over to them as Mr Goodwin began to make the strangest sound. Soft snorts and odd breaths.

He was laughing.

I put my books away then and listened to the rest of the conversation, nodding and adding a few words when they glanced over at me with interested eyes.

After that I still took my homework, but it normally stayed in my bag. A few weeks on, when I kissed him goodbye Mr Goodwin patted a hand on my shoulder. Looking back now, I should have realised a lot sooner. But I was young and still had little experience of older people. It wasn't until Dad got sent on a particular errand that it clicked.

One afternoon when we arrived Mr Goodwin was looking agitated. At first he wouldn't say what the problem was, but with some coaxing from Mum, it emerged that the prescription service had missed an item from his delivery and he'd have to wait until the following day to get it if he couldn't pick it up from the pharmacy. Dad sprang up without so much as a look from Mum. It was humid that day and I went with him to get some fresher air, car windows rolled all the way down, hair sticking to the back of my damp neck.

The pharmacy was quiet, just us and one man behind the counter, taking things from boxes and putting them in other boxes. When Dad gave Mr Goodwin's name the man nodded and smiled apologetically, thanking us for coming in. He handed the missing item over and Dad took it, then froze. He read the name out as if to confirm it was right, but it was a statement, not a question.

'Oramorph.'

The name meant nothing to me, but Dad obviously knew what it was. I knew, then – from the way he shook his head and rubbed his fingers over his eyes. We didn't speak on the journey home.

Mr Goodwin gave us a sad smile when we got back. Mum was sitting in the chair next to his, leaning towards him. She held one of his hands gently in hers. From the barely held back tears, I knew they'd been chatting.

It all looked so different to me then. The messier than usual kitchen. The grime around the bathroom taps. These things only became apparent when I started looking for them – he'd never struggled before. It turned out he was having home help now. A couple of carers, twice a week. We stepped up our visits, too. Mum brought casseroles. If he wasn't too tired, we would stay to eat with Mr Goodwin, before Mum made sure he had everything he needed for the night.

I last saw him on a Tuesday afternoon after school. It was September and the days were getting shorter. I had my thick black cardigan on over my blouse. Mr Goodwin's bed was in the front room by then.

I pulled a stool close so he wouldn't have to talk too loudly or strain to hear. I think he knew, because he was finding it difficult to meet my gaze again. I was thinking about leaving him to rest when he looked up at me with a grin.

'Did I ever tell you about when I worked in my Dad's sweet shop?'

I shook my head and he reached over to take my hand. His was warm and softer than I'd imagined. He told me about his younger brother – 'he ate more toffees than he sold! – giggling away. I giggled too, although I wanted to cry.

Mr Goodwin told me to be a good girl for my parents and to make sure I went to university. It was important.

When Dad came to pick me up Mr Goodwin squeezed my hand once before letting go. Then a surprised look came over his face and he raised a hand and lightly tugged on one of the loose brown curls that had fallen away from the rest of my bun. He seemed to be lost in thought or dreams or memories, smiling sleepily up at me.

Emily Cotterill

Welfare

By the time the sign finally fell
it was several decades out of date.
Knocked to the ground by a football
booted over a low fence by a boy
who should have been in school.
They say in '88 the man sent to fetch it
crashed on the A617. So it hung on.
Over graffiti on boarded windows,
teenage lovers turned to couples married,
or divorced – tiles slipped, foundations sunk.
I drank cans carrying that brand
on unmowed grass around the back
but I was long gone for the fall.
A spectacle nobody saw, heavy letters
making holes in the concrete floor.

Footpath To Shining Cliff Woods

Grass grows back over soft tyre tracks.
This year, of course, the road is louder
but for the sake of a girl, a dog and a father,
all sound disappears. We are invading history,
rewilding our biology.
Every year a piece of flora takes back over:
corrugated iron crumbles, orange dust on
a cracked concrete floor. When I was a child
I think I knew what this factory was for but now,
it invites archaeology. The mushrooms sprout,
blackberries stain our faces and this year
there are more sweet chestnuts
than we ever gathered before.
Early on we crush their cases in damp leaves,
encouraging the compost with our plastic heels
but when the sun begins to set we bend,
lowering the weight on aching hind legs
and pry apart tiny presents, hardened fingers,
feeble spines.
I throw the dog a stick through an empty window—
one year, not far from now, the collie dashes in,
an ancient wolf stalks out.

Ashleigh Davies

Not Forever

Sonic boom and the scent of phosphorous,
a nettle of fallout kissing our scalps,
bracketing fear to our chests, a quickening
sensation. More like a white water rapid
than the detonation of a bedside monitor.
In seconds our skin is raw and scrubbed pink.

Hypersensitivity drilled into our fingertips,
each touch a raking of scorched
iron filings, voltage cracking
through the nervous system. I could power
the National Grid through my mesh of veins,
synapses rewired to hadron collision.

Body strung for lightning rods and seems of
brimstone;
the patio is a furl of ash and hot swarf crowds
the base of each stem. In winters to come—
roots, rotting with nuclear decay, thaw.
My child says *quick, the floor is lava—*
and we haven't got forever.

Lonely Hours

Pluralities

Here we dismiss pluralities.
We are a desperation of people
As we alight the train.

Our slowly combusting membrane
Of bodies flood the platform

Amid this economy of words
Your mouth is full of diamonds

Black birds perch on the lines
Feeling for the wave
Of a new train.

Conversations

Anyways the cement set
And there she was
Plain as day or the nose
On your face

I buys them in bulk, see—
Pallets at a time, so
If you're ever stuck,
I'm the one you need
To call on

Sorrow and Joy

Always in transit
These monochrome vagabonds
Appear to me.

Yin-yang units
Of pure superstition.

It takes me two claps
And a rabbit's foot
To purge their bad fortune

Commonalities

Midnight;
Me and my doppelganger
On the platform

And how curious to find
Us here, at this lonely hour;
One set west, and me

Seeking out the fox.
His covert snout smeared
With grime, mouth set
In an exhausted grin.

Until startled by the Miles Davis
Cry of an owl.

My doppelganger hears it too.
Climbs into my skin
Holds on for his life

And mine.

Could be Anything

She told herself not to assume the worst, that it could be anything. Emily stood in front of her bathroom mirror on tip-toes and lifted her arm, appraising her ribs side-on. It wasn't even visible. She flattened the skin as best she could, holding the swelling between index and middle finger. Her face had gravitated so close to the reflected image that the mirror had begun to steam up. She told herself again it could be anything, this time speaking aloud. If Gareth was here he would be calling her crazy for talking to herself. She continued to speak, telling herself that it could be a blemish, an ingrown hair even. It couldn't happen to somebody twice, could it?

Spinning herself back around, she viewed her naked torso front-on. Her chest looked like an unfinished map after the mastectomy. She hadn't so much as contemplated cosmetic surgery. The last thing she wanted was to go under the knife again.

'It could be anything, she said again with finality.

Three weeks later and she could still feel it, like an itch that couldn't be reached. Her daily inspection had become a fixture of her morning ritual. She would get up, brush her teeth, shower, and check the lump. The more she told herself that it could be anything, the more things she began to rule out. Too big for a zit, too pale for a bruise. She told herself not to worry. It couldn't be a tumour. There wasn't even a name for this kind of thing. Sure there was breast cancer, and throat cancer, cancer of the blood, but there was no just-below-the-armpit cancer was there? Emily asked herself if she was healthy enough. Her inspections became interrogations. Did she drink too much wine? Did she not drink enough? Did she need to exercise more?

Six weeks after she had first noticed it in the shower she decided to tell Gareth. They were on the sofa, having just finished dinner. Their dishes were piled atop one another on the coffee table, waiting to be taken out. There was a celebrity talk show on television. Gareth was browsing the Internet on his laptop.

'Will you take a look at something for me?' she asked. Gareth continued to scroll down the page, his face paled by the glow of the screen.

'Sure, what is it?' he asked. When he used the laptop Gareth would wear his glasses low on the bridge of his nose. He sat up and pushed his spectacles further up his nose. Emily tried to act calm, pulling her legs up onto the sofa.

'I was taking a shower and I felt something.'

Gareth slapped the laptop shut and laid it on the coffee table, next to the plates.

'What is it?'

Emily hitched her sweatshirt up and slid her arm free to expose the lump to Gareth. He leaned in closer and followed Emily's fingertip as she traced a circle around the swelling.

'I can't really see anything, does it hurt?' he asked. Emily took his hand and pressed it over the swollen area, carefully navigating his fingers over the lump.

'It's tender if I touch it,' she said.

'Should we get it checked?' Gareth asked.

Emily wasn't sure what she had wanted from the

exchange, but this wasn't it. She did not want to go back to the hospital; more scans, the whooping of the MRI machine. She shrugged.

'I don't know,' she said.

'It could be anything,' Gareth said.

*

Most of the party-goers were in the kitchen. It was Gareth's brother's birthday and he had thrown a party. Emily had made her way upstairs to the main bedroom. The bed was a tapestry of multi-coloured coats. She took a sip of wine from a plastic cup. Her teeth were stained red. There was a full-length mirror on the back of the door. Emily put her cup down on the nightstand and surveyed her reflection. The dress she wore wasn't hanging like it was supposed to. She felt even more lopsided than usual. She hated wearing dresses now, but did so to prove a point. She wasn't about to stop being a woman, just because she'd had a breast removed. There was a whole lot more to being a woman than the body she had found herself in. She lifted the dress up and over her hips, sliding it from her chest to expose the mark. It could be seen now, as well as felt. In the dim light of the bedroom it was nothing more than a shadow though. She flinched as the door opened. It was Gareth. He looked at her knowingly as she allowed her dress to fall back into place.

'Are you okay? I didn't know where you went,' he said.

'Yeah I'm fine,' she answered.

'Is it still there?'

'It's nothing.'

'Are you sure? Because we can go and get it checked. Best to be safe.'

Emily shook her head.

'I already did,' she lied. 'Swollen gland or something like that. It'll go eventually.'

Gareth seemed to deflate with relief. He set his cup down on the nightstand next to Emily's and walked towards her.

'Well that's good news,' he said, pulling her towards him. 'Why didn't you tell me? I would have come with you.'

Emily pulled herself closer to him so that she could smell the aftershave on his shirt.

'I didn't want to worry you,' she said.

*

Emily poked at her chow mein with a chopstick. The work canteen was a chorus of conversations.

'Do you still speak to Kevin?' Emily asked. She would take lunch with Sarah at least once a week. They had gone through university together and both ended up interning at the same design studio. Three years later and they still came as a pair.

'You mean the pot-head from second year?' Sarah asked. She had bulging eyes that made her look sort of frog-like.

'Yeah,' Emily answered.

Sarah frowned, stuffing a fork-full of salad leaves into her cheek. Emily compared herself to Sarah in the way that friends often did. She felt brittle and sharp, positively angular in comparison.

'Not really, he was harmless and all but what a waster.'

Emily took a sip of diet cola. 'I wonder what he's doing now?'

'You'll never believe it, but he's a warden at the halls of residence,' Sarah replied.

‘At the university still?’

Sarah laughed. She had a strange sort of smirk that she wore when amused, smiling with only half her mouth.

‘Yeah. It’s funny because he used to joke about how he’d never leave.’

*

The halls were exactly as Emily had remembered, banks of two-tiered grey-brick apartments. Each one had been named after an historic county of Wales. She had been in Pembrokeshire when she studied. Emily had needed to ask five students before she found out that Kevin was the warden in Cardiganshire. She had waited outside of the main entrance for a student to enter, following her in before the latch closed. The warden’s flat was always the first door you would come to. Emily knocked. She was relieved when Kevin did answer, looking exactly like he had years ago. He had a camouflage jacket on and oversized shorts. He looked at Emily with the gaze of someone who only half knew where they were.

‘Emily?’ he asked with a turn of the head, hedging his bets.

‘You remembered,’ she answered, picking at her sleeve.

‘I haven’t seen you in ages!’ he said. Kevin had the look of a permanently exhausted person. His skin had an ashen hue that made the dark bags under his eyes look menacing. He was sporting a shaved head and a lip-ring.

‘Yeah I know. Did you ever graduate?’ she joked. Kevin laughed his hyena-laugh. It was like a time-warp. Emily felt pulled towards the exit, that bad-idea feeling in her stomach.

‘Are you looking for anyone?’ Kevin asked.

'Well actually, I'm looking for you.'

'Right, well come in.' Kevin said, opening the door and inviting Emily into the room. She had no idea how a flat so small could get so messy. Not a square inch of carpet was visible beneath the mesh of clothes that he been strewn on the floor. A pile of polystyrene take-away boxes had engulfed the waste-paper bin.

'Sorry about the mess, I should be setting a better example really.' Kevin cleared a pile of clothes off his desk-chair and gestured for Emily to take a seat. She sat, clutching her purse close to her chest. Kevin hadn't seemed to have aged at all.

'So what are you doing now?' Kevin asked, sitting cross-legged on his bed.

'I'm a design consultant at a fashion website,' she answered proudly.

'Very nice, you did that when you were here didn't you?'

'Yeah, me and Sarah, we work together now.'

'That's great, I liked Sarah a lot. We were in the same flats in second year. Anyway, what do you want me for?' he asked.

'This is going to sound crazy,' Emily began, playing with the clasp of her purse. 'Do you still smoke?'

'You mean green, yeah?' he asked.

Emily smiled nervously.

'Yeah.'

'I've been known to partake from time to time. Why?' Kevin asked. His smile was goofy with the lip-ring dangling from his mouth – crammed too full of teeth.

'I was just wondering where I could get some.'

'Really, you get high?' he asked, the hyena in him making another appearance.

'No, not like that. I mean, medicinal stuff. I don't

really know the difference but I thought it may be worth a try.'

Kevin furrowed his brows.

'I guess I could put my hands on some, but what for, you sick?'

Emily put her bag down on the floor. The two of them sat in silence for a short while. Muffled voices could be heard from the next room.

'I think I have cancer,' Emily answered. She had surprised even herself with the confession. The revelation was unplanned, but now it was out she felt a booming liberation on her chest. Kevin blew a puff of air out of his cheeks and looked around the room.

'I'm so sorry,' he said. An awkward hand crawled across to alight on Emily's knee before being sharply removed. Emily nodded. She tried to figure out why she had told Kevin. It made no sense. She had lied to Gareth, and to Sarah. She continued all the same. Kevin shifted over to Emily and hugged her, more softly than she would have thought possible.

'I've had it before,' she said.

Kevin shook his head. Emily put down her purse. Before she could make sense of it, her jumper had been pulled over her head and she had undone her bra. She let it fall to the ground, camouflaged amongst the throng of other garments. Only Gareth had seen her naked after the mastectomy, now here she was showing her scars to a man she barely knew. She took Kevin's hand and pressed it against her chest, pulling it over the braille of her scars.

'I'm so sorry,' he said again.

*

Raindrops were dappling the roof of the tent. Emily tried to count them, but they came so fast and in such great numbers that it was impossible. Gareth was sleeping next to her. She had learnt to understand his sleeping pattern. The low hum of his shallow dreaming would soon give way to the tractor-roar of his deep-sleep snore. They had come out to the countryside to camp with Sarah and her new squeeze. Emily had drunk too much wine; she could feel it bloating her stomach. She was experiencing the strange sensation she associated with being at the centre of a playground roundabout. She was still but the space around her was churning. She took Gareth's descent into earnest snoring as her cue, sliding her body from beneath the unzipped sleeping bag. The air outside was clammy and cold. Emily reached furtively towards the Velcro door of the tent. She peeled it open, like ripping a plaster from a wound. Carefully she crawled towards the exit and shuffled over the threshold and into the rain. It was quieter outside, without the constant shuffle of showers against canvas. Emily edged forwards on her knees, a scree of mud and twigs stuck to the exposed skin of her legs. She had performed this exercise on a number of occasions back home, so that it was now carefully practiced and easy. She dared not light the cigarette too close to the tents, pitched adjacent to one another and glittering with rainfall. Emily made towards a wooded enclave a hundred or so yards away, pulling her woollen sweater tighter around her torso.

Once beneath a mottled canopy of stunted trees she took the tin from the pocket of the shorts she was wearing. Inside was a single hand-rolled cigarette. It was the last of the most recent batch that Kevin had rolled. Emily would visit him once a fortnight now. She would sit on his bed and play video games, pretending to go back in time. Forgetting the lump on her side. He would roll the cigarettes for her and pack them into a tin, enough to get by until the next visit. She stood in the gloom of the trees and lit the cigarette, toking shallow lungfuls of smoke. If this was her new favourite pastime, then considering the consequences of her growth was a close second. She would mull over the scans, the therapy. She would think about the drawer full of pamphlets her consultant would offer – none of which would be read. She would get so far before being arrested by an uncanny sense of déjà vu.

Deep into the forest a stirring of leaves and bracken alerted Emily. She peered hard into the foliage; the forest was all glimmer and sepia. She heard the stirring again, feeling the movement at a distance in the way one may feel a storm brewing in the next valley. Emily stubbed the cigarette against a tree bark and discarded it onto the ground. She crouched and listened carefully. A short time went by with no further sound. Emily raised herself to her full height and shrugged her shoulders, trying to discard the eerie disconcertion she had experienced. She realised the rain had stopped. The only sound was the gliding wind, playing the trees like a pan-flute. She finally backed away, telling herself that it could be anything. It could be nothing at all.

Rhodri Diaz

Bring Me the Head of Dylan Thomas

The morning we found Dylan Thomas's head in our back garden was like any other in the old seaside town; bright and cold and pregnant with promise. We had just emerged from the dog days of summer, the kind of summer where unsticking our legs from Mamgu's leather sofa was a Herculean task, and the first stiff breeze of Autumn felt like new life was being injected into our tired bones. There was nothing about this particular morning that prefigured a mystery, and it started in familiar fashion: with the first chords of 'Don't Stop Believin'' by Journey ringing in my ears. His unique choice of alarm was just one of the many features that made my brother an absolute delight to share a room with. After I'd lobbed a Mickey Mouse snow globe at his head, I stumbled to the window and ripped the curtains open. The sudden rush of pale sunlight stung my eyes. Guto grumbled and rolled over, cocooning himself in the duvet.

That's when I saw it. A hunk of dull grey metal lying on its side in the dewy grass. It was speckled with mud and someone had scrawled a swear word on its forehead with pink paint. From my vantage point, I could just about make out its features, and recognised the same man who had been staring out at me from a battered school copy of *Under Milk Wood* for the last three weeks.

I hopped onto Guto's bed and tried to shake him awake. He swatted wildly, grunting and groaning and turning the air blue. I dodged and ducked his flailing arms with the speed and grace of Muhammad Ali until, finally, he managed to catch me in a tight headlock and I was forced to admit defeat.

'Geroff me.' My head was wedged firmly into Guto's armpit, the mingled scent of stale sweat and Lynx Africa polluting my airways.

'Piss off, Ianto.' He let go of my head and shoved me off the bed. I fell with a heavy thud, and immediately felt a bruise forming on my left arse-cheek.

'You're a wanker, you are,' he said, before yanking the duvet over his head and rolling over defiantly. Arse still aching, I positioned myself gingerly on the edge of the bed before picking my words as delicately as possible.

'There's a head in the garden'

'No, there isn't,' he said from under the duvet.

'There is, though. It's Dylan Thomas'.'

It was so silent, I could practically hear the cogs turning in Guto's brain. Once he had a chance to process what I had said, he responded in typical fashion by kicking the duvet off dramatically and stomping to the window.

'I swear to God, if there's no bloody head in this garden, I'm going to punch you in the chops.'

He looked out of the window, and the colour drained from his face until it resembled watery porridge.

'There's a head in the garden.'

'I told you.' Guto balled up his fist and gritted his teeth. After a few seconds, he calmed down and continued staring out of the window, lips moving soundlessly.

'That's off the statue down the Marina,' I said.

I joined him at the window and we stood in deafening

silence, both trying to devise some possible reason why a statue's head was occupying space in our back garden. After what seemed like an eternity, Guto bolted for the door.

'Where are you off?' I asked.

'We need to get rid of the bloody thing, don't we? Anyone sees that, they'll peg it on us.'

I followed closely as Guto tramped downstairs. When he reached the bottom step, he picked up my school bag and thrust it into my chest.

'Go and get it.'

I stumbled backwards and tried to hold on to the banister for support. I shoved the rucksack at Guto, but he anticipated it and stepped out of the way, leaving me to fall flat on my face.

'Why do I have to get it?' I whined, rubbing my stinging nose.

'Because I'm not dressed.'

'Neither am I!'

Guto yanked me up by the collar of my pyjama top and shepherded me towards the back door. He reached for the doorknob, but something stopped him.

'Where's Mam?' he asked.

Mam worked nights at the nursing home down the road every Tuesday, Wednesday and Thursday. It kept us going, for the most part. She had a routine when she came home, and she never deviated from it. She would creep in quietly so as not to disturb us, hang her keys up on the hook next to the door, stick her headphones on, crank up the radio and flop onto the sofa, where she'd pass out for a good few hours. It was a ritual, regimented, which made it even more worrying that she wasn't there that morning, and her keys weren't on the hook. I looked at Guto, and he registered the panic in my eyes. For a moment, his face softened and I wondered if he was going to speak words of comfort, but instead he opened the back door and shoved me out.

'This is our chance. Put it in the bag, quick as you can,' he shouted, before shutting the door on me.

I saw him through the window, trotting to the kitchen and pouring out a bowl of Frosties that he picked at one by one as he skipped back upstairs to change.

I crouched down next to the head, and examined it closely. There was a chip missing from its nose, residual damage from whatever misfortune had befallen it. The area around the neck was jagged and spiky. It looked like someone had knocked it off with brute force. It was so cold from sitting outside all night that holding it stung my fingers, so I opened the rucksack and bundled it in. I remembered too late that my homework for Mrs Watkins was in there, now filthy and sopping wet. Trying not to imagine the bollocking I was going to get from my least favourite teacher, I slipped back inside and found Guto perched on the kitchen counter, fully dressed and drinking milk straight from the bottle. I put the bag next to him on the counter and snatched the milk from his hands.

'Not meant to do that,' I said.

He snorted and hopped off the counter, watching intently as I made a big song and dance of putting the milk back into the fridge. Throwing the bag on his back, he picked up a biscuit jar in the shape of a Beatrix Potter character and started rummaging around inside.

'You just had Frosties, you fat git.'

He pulled a £20 note from the jar and held it up for me to inspect.

'Mam's secret stash. Not so secret anymore.' There

was a glint in his eye as he stuffed the note into his pocket. He picked up a corner of the doormat with the precision of a crime scene investigator and fished out the spare key. I was half way up the stairs when I heard the rattle of the key in the door.

'I'm not dressed yet!' I shouted, but Guto had already bolted. I grabbed my duffle coat and the nearest pair of shoes I could find and threw them on as quickly as I could.

I struggled to keep up with him as he motored down the street. Unfortunately, the nearest pair of shoes were Mam's pink flip flops, and they were not conducive to fast movement. I shouted at Guto to slow down, but he ignored me. He had neglected to share with me his master plan, but I assumed we were heading for the train station. We would often head into town with Mam on her days off, and wander aimlessly through the market, the scent of the fish stall thick in the air. Without fail, Mam would go to the bakery and buy us a Swansea Pie each and a bag of Welshcakes, and we'd eat them on the train home while they were still warm, fingers sticky from the sugar. This, however, was the first time we'd attempted to travel to town on our own, and I felt anxiety creep in slowly and settle in my chest.

The station was heaving, and I could feel my chest tighten as we weaved between the throng of people to-ing and fro-ing. Guto paid for the tickets at the self-service machine to avoid any awkward questions. The guard at the barriers gave us a funny look, but we stared at the floor and beat on through the crowd. I strained to hear the announcements over the screech of gullsong overhead. Our train was delayed by two minutes. Guto perched himself on a bench and I settled down next to him, wedging the bag between our legs.

We sat in silence and I watched a man in a tweed suit try and chat up a woman who was talking on her phone. He was leaning into her so closely that she was forced to press herself up against a pillar. I thought about going to talk to her, because I heard that's what you're meant to do when that's happening, go and talk to the person to make them feel less scared, but then I remembered I was wearing pyjamas and pink flip-flops and thought better of it. He got bored and wandered off eventually, and a weight visibly lifted off her shoulders.

Finally, the train pulled into the station, brakes wailing so loudly that they completely drowned out the sound of the seagulls. Guto immediately leapt on to the train, pushing past a group of blue-rinsed women out on a daytrip. Cursing his name, I picked up the bag and heard the terrifying sound of material ripping and stitches rending. The head made an immense clattering noise as it struck the ground. I watched in silence as it rolled across the floor and stopped at the feet of a fine upstanding member of the British Transport Police. We stood staring at each other for what felt like an eternity. His eyes flicked erratically between me, the head and the torn bag. Coming to my senses, I yelled for Guto, who had been watching the entire drama in abject horror. We raced past the stunned policeman and vaulted over the security barrier, dodging the guard who made a pathetic attempt at grabbing us, before weaving our way through the crowd and out of the door.

We ran for what felt like hours. My legs burned, and my heart beat hard in my chest. As we rounded a corner, I found myself running straight into what felt like a brick wall. Dazed, I looked up and saw Mathew Parsons looming over me. Mathew was big-boned, lumpy-headed and used the gifts God had granted him to be a proper dickhead to all and sundry. Guto had carried on running, but when he heard the commotion, he dashed back to see if I was okay. Mathew's giant frame blocked his path, and he was quickly enveloped in the mass of humanity that stood before him.

'Got the little present I left for you, Williams?' he sneered. He'd caught Guto in a full-nelson and was shaking him about.

'Piss off, wanker,' Guto snapped back, arms flailing as Mathew tightened his vice-like hold.

'I thought it'd be a lovely centrepiece for your garden.'

'You left that there?' I asked. Mathew dropped Guto face first and took an obnoxious bow. Guto took advantage of the distraction, spun him around and gave him a right wallop. Mathew stumbled backwards, and I saw the blood start to ooze out of his nose. Red mist descending, he darted forward, buried a fist deep into Guto's gut and lifted him up by the collar. I spied my opportunity. I grabbed the torn bag, crept up behind him and yanked it right over his head. He yelped and howled like a wounded dog, and we made for the safety of the house.

Once inside, we were greeted by the ominous sight of Mam being comforted by a policeman. It turned out that she had worked a little bit later than usual, and had come home to find our beds empty and the two of us nowhere to be found. The policeman questioned us both, and we had to go down the station to make statements, and all I can remember is how his breath stank of coffee and fags. Mam shouted, and then hugged us, and then shouted more and we were grounded for the rest of our lives, or so it felt like. The obscene vandalism of Dylan Thomas' statue made front page news in the South Wales Evening Post. But then Mrs Jones Next Door's cat once made front page of the South Wales Evening Post, so that's not saying a lot. CCTV caught Mathew Parsons in the act of taking a crowbar to old Dylan Thomas, and he's doing his community service as part of a graffiti removal team. My brother and I never really spoke about what had happened, but that night, when we were both in bed, he reached his hand out towards me, and I offered mine in response. We gave each other an affectionate squeeze and both of us understood. Not long after, he gave me an atomic wedgie.

Mari Ellis Dunning

Afterparty

after Zelda Fitzgerald

One by one, this string of sticky pearls clogged the
gullet of your golden girl, hissing like champagne—

I tried to sleep through the sunrise, wanted nothing
more than to curl in to myself, pliéd beneath the duvet.

I hoped you would find me there, splayed and beautiful,
an eyelash beaten loose by the drag of my palm,

one leg impossibly kinked, bruised still from the
clatter of marble stairs, demanding, always, all the
iridescence of the beginning of the world.

Mizuko

In traditional Japanese teachings, Mizuko statues are believed to be protectors of children and unborn babies. It is believed that as the babies did not have the chance to build up good karma on earth, Jizo helps smuggle the children into the afterlife in the sleeves of his robe.

for a day or two he was lost and wandering, a mote of dust in a dark vacuum,

for a while, i was a fish floundering for air, a speck of nothing at all, and so

we marched. Heads bowed and lolling, we laid our griefs at the feet

of Mizuko Jizō, folded our water child in to the Buddha's gaping sleeves;

palm to palm, we fell in to a cherry blossom haze, slept the sleep of the dead.

Lingering

I couldn't stand the cedarwood stench that grew in your absence, so I migrated, birdlike, to the smaller back bedroom.

Each night, I hear your shallow breath seeping through the thin wall, picture you, one leg cocked, reaching for me through darkness.

I found your keyring lying under the sofa, gathering dust, forgotten, and on it – that photo of us, of you,

a bearded stranger, and me, girlish and unsure, cloaked in a vintage dress awaiting assurance of my beauty.

With oversized marigolds and an old tea towel, I bleached your skin cells from the skirting boards, swabbed the residue

of you from the foundations. You clung like smoke to the wallpaper. Exhausted, I collapsed, wondering if you had been exorcised

yet. Willing you to throw open the front door,
to call out, 'I'm home.'

Emily Hancox

Suffragette

In commemoration to all those who defended my voice, long before I could speak.

I'll stand beside you.
Speak when you're too worn
when countries burden you
when history re-writes your legacy,
I will stand in your stead.
Lead those into unity
Hold composure
and while others turn and forget
I will always speak of your victories.
I will carry you
on my voice,
as my strength and my memory.
Though your politics, your leaders
And your own
might discriminate
I refuse to cover, turn my back on you.
One torch might burn in dark solitude
But if held high
It can spark the actions
of millions.

Kimberley Houlihan

Birdwatching

'Birdwatching?' I said, and her shoulders did that thing that they do, jerking up towards her ears. My wife is the only person I have ever known to literally put her back up when on the defence.

'What's wrong with that?' She replied.

What's wrong with that? We're in our thirties for starters. When I'd said we should try going out a bit more, this was exactly the type of premature aging activity that I had been hoping to avoid. We had started spending a lot of evenings wearing our slippers in front of the telly, watching crime dramas sponsored by Viking Cruises. When I said 'let's go out a bit more,' I was thinking a mid-week trip to the cinema. But her jaw line was sinking into her collar bone by this point, so I didn't argue.

'That sounds interesting,' I said. Another hundred quid wasted on kit that would end up in the cupboard with the Pilates ball and the bread maker.

She found this local group online, the 'Titchy Twitchers'. 'Oh,' she said, 'Isn't it cute?' I did offer to accompany her on the first meet, but I had a deadline at work to prepare for and she insisted that she would be okay to scope them out herself. And then things just sort of escalated.

Her alarm went off in the deepest hours of the night, well-before dawn. I'd watch her silhouette as she dressed in the dark bedroom, moonlight from the window licking at goose bumps on her back. The arch of flat muscle across her stomach. I'd listen as she tiptoed down into the kitchen, hear the tinkling of cutlery as she prepared and ate a quiet breakfast. I'd get up when the glare of the headlights reversed away from the curtains, onto the road.

She started keeping something called a 'life list.' Basically, a list of all the birds she saw. Apparently it's a big deal in, you know, birdwatching. And then she started coming home with facts: did I know that the eye of a peregrine was bigger than a human eye? I was glad, truth be told. Glad that we were talking over dinner again. Glad that she would pause the crime drama to tell me more about her day. I started feeling lighter than I had in months. I was singing along with the radio on the commute home from work each day, whistling in the shower, making small talk in the office. That was until last Thursday.

Thursday evening, to be exact, I was in the middle of a mouthful of broad beans. She'd been talking about the nest formations of wrens, when she said, 'luckily, Pete always carries this really fancy camera, so we were able to get some amazing shots.'

'Pete?' I said. You do think of men, don't you, when you think of birdwatching? But they're all retired, aren't they? Or they wear those hats with wide brims, their trousers rolled up over their ankles. Not men men. Men men in the 'Titchy Twitchers'? But Pete—Pete's ex-navy.

'Retired?' I asked, picking the bean skin from my teeth.

'No, he's forty, maybe. He injured his hand saving a friends life out in the jungle somewhere. He never went back.'

I said, 'Tell me more about the wren.'

So Saturday there I was, sat next to her in the car, following those headlights to Bishop's Wood. The roads were dead. We didn't see a soul, save for a single fox helping himself to the contents of a shredded bin bag. It's weird being up at that time. As we drove through silent streets, I found myself willing the engine to be quieter, as if we were doing something wrong and I didn't want to get caught. Imagine the contrast then, when we pulled into this carpark in the middle of nowhere, to find it bustling with activity. For one horrifying second, I thought that we had stumbled into a dogger's meeting. I swore. She didn't find it funny when I explained.

There were six other vehicles, their owners standing out in the cold shuffling maps and fiddling with binoculars. A nodding dog wobbled at us from the back window of an over-polished Corsa. These were the Twitchers that I had been expecting: short, pot-bellied men with mole-ish mannerisms. We jumped out of the car and made our way over to them, avoiding the slippery patches of frozen-over potholes. Our companions seemed to shrink away as we approached, as if we held some magical ancient artefact. She offered a wide-smile hello and one of them actually seemed to swoon. The girl I met five years ago in a bar was stepping out in front of me, as if she were shedding a skin. And then a tall figure appeared from behind a Land Rover, a muscle-riddled torso in a blue North Face jacket.

'Hi,' it said. 'I'm Pete.'

We followed Pete in silence as dawn finally broke. He wore these tight trousers, his arse threatening to burst out at any moment as he quietly pumped his way uphill. Every now and again he would stop and raise his hand to the group behind him who would all stand to attention, like meerkats. Then he would gesture with his fingers before pointing, and their heads would snap simultaneously into his chosen direction. It was tiring, the mud sucked at my new mountain boots and my nose was beginning to itch, bringing with it the realisation that I had forgotten to take my antihistamine. And worse than that, there was nothing to see! Sure, you could hear plenty of birds, but we were looking at branches. Eventually, I had to speak up.

'What exactly are we looking at?' I asked.

'Oh, for God's sake,' she said.

'Never mind,' Pete sighed.

'What?' I said.

'Maybe we should split up?' A Twitcher offered.

I was only too bloody glad. I went with the wife, of course, leaving Pete and his arse with some bloke sporting an attempted beard.

'What did you do that for?' she asked.

'I couldn't see anything,' I explained, but she wasn't listening, not really.

Her eyes were fixed firmly ahead, her lips stretched thin and tight as she picked her way through dogwood. She looked old and hard and some buzzing thing, an inexplicable aura, spiked out from her. The Twitchers wouldn't recognise this person. No, this was not my bride – the woman who had kissed me beneath cherry blossoms as our family and friends looked on in pride and envy. This was not the girl who had downed my drink at the bar, winked and led me to the dance floor with a cool, supple stride. Those thick, firm thighs brazen beneath her skirt. Those eyes beckoning me in, sirens calling me to wander with them. Who was this woman? The imposter in our home? The empty shell in our bed?

We walked shrouded in bright birdsong. The sun was peeling out, promising a good day, but it was still freezing. My fingers had turned numb and my heels burned with blisters. We should pack it in, I thought. Go home. But then I realised that she had stopped – a statue amongst the bracken cast golden by morning light. She stood with her hand clamped to her mouth. Her eyes trained down just like the detectives we watched. I caught up with her, followed her gaze.

A broken nest spewed on to the forest floor, a firework of twigs, web and leaves. At its centre was a shattered shell, a purple-pink dribble jutting out onto the dirt. A tiny beak. A deep, black eye.

She began to cry.

Niall Ivin

Fly-Tipping

Darren looked across the cab.

'Reckon you could catch a sheep?'

Carl squinted at him and shook his head.

'Go on mun, d'you reckon? I reckon I could, if I needed to like. Reckon you could?'

Carl shook his head again.

'I've seen you at full back.'

Rubbish bags filled the van. All the detritus of discarded living piled like a necrotic cairn, heaving with each movement the van made. Bits of wood and plastic protruded from it, a bouquet of arrows in a hunted, discarded animal.

'Did you sort those bags out tidy or what?' Darren craned his neck to look, 'if there's a bloody mess in there you'll be sorting it.'

He broke hard at the cattle grid and the van lurched over itself. A slat stabbed into the cabin, smashing the dashboard. Darren flashed a churlish grin and shook his head.

'Bloody 'ell.'

They trundled forward and the headlights revealed a large wooden sign.

Welcome to Twmbarlwm. Please take all litter away with you. Respect the landscape. Thank you.

The headlights bobbed past and spilled into the pastures on either side of the road. Glaring eyes nestled low in the gloom watched them pass. Then they illuminated the scarred remains of the forest.

'Terrible ain't it?' said Darren.

Carl looked at the stumps. Rows of them, lined up like prisoners for execution. Small branches and twigs caked the forest floor, prostrate and mourning.

'Makes it a bit hard to look at don't it. Like looking at an amputee or something,' said Darren. 'The ol' man used to ride his crosser up here, before I was born. Used to cut the place up a treat, locals fuckin' hated it!' He laughed. 'Your ol' man bring you up here when you was little?'

'Aye. Used to walk up way ahead of us to prove a point. Me and him chucked the dogs ashes where it overlooks the estate. He used to say he'd want his put up there too, before—'

'Looks like it's just us.'

Darren pulled up onto the grass and switched everything off. Darkness collapsed on them.

'We'll wait a minute now, just in case.'

Their eyes gradually adjusted to the darkness. The outline of the old motte exposed itself, as did the thin strip of forestry that remained.

'They may as well 'av lopped off that last bit really,'

'Could say the same about that bit you've got left there,' said Carl, prodding Darren's head. Darren leaned away and frowned.

'Let's crack on.'

The bags slumped against each other, torn and twisted. Darren tried to separate them but a plume of grey powder burst out, like a primitive defence mechanism. He threw it, spluttering, wafting the spores away.

Carl looked at the outline of the motte. The day they'd walked up there it was clear, but windy. His dad carried the ashes in a rucksack and he'd tried hard to keep pace. When they stopped, they talked about the dog's first walk, and the view and making dens in the forest. He thought about how the ashes caught the wind. How they diffused out over the valley. How it blew back and threw a good portion into their faces. He thought about what his dad asked him to do, when the time came.

'On parade ya lazy shite, the sooner we chuck all this the better,' Darren chastised him.

Carl walked around to the back of the van and looked at the broken, sagging things hanging out of it. Things that won't mourn their time and then go away. These things would outlast the motte. They'd outlast the earthworks from a thousand thousand years ago. He looked at Darren.

'I don't know if we should,'

'Don't be daft mun. Someone will be up in the morning and they'll sort it. The ramblers and the farmers and that, they'll sort it.'

'It's not right Dar'.'

Darren stopped.

'I ain't payin' half a ton to get rid of all this crap. No fuckin' chance.'

'I'll pay to get rid of it, I'll pay for it.'

'You can't afford that you daft sod.'

Carl started snatching the bags off the floor and throwing them into the van.

'Why the fuck do you care anyway?' said Darren.

Carl grabbed the last bag off the floor. Darren sprang at him and gripped it, the plastic tearing, spilling its innards. Carl dropped to his hands and knees, scrabbling to pick up what he could. Darren watched, with the plastic still ragged in his hand.

'What the fuck is wrong with you?' said Darren.

'I don't know.'

'It's just a bit of scrap, Carl.'

'Yeah, it is. Exactly.'

Katya Johnson

The Silver Darlings

(First Prize)

September 1876, Borth Morfa

The first time I saw him he was leaning against the keel of his boat *Ruth*, wearing a dusty suit, with his hat cocked at a slant on his head, gazing out to sea. He caught me looking and called out 'Hey you! Boy!' but I was afraid and ran away as fast as my legs could carry me, down along the shingle spit. That was in spring before the arrival of the herring harvest in autumn. I could tell because suddenly the grey beach was awash with small boats, sloops and fishing smacks. This time he was not alone but with a friend. I heard him whisper to him: 'Look 'e, over there, that's the one I was talking about,' and saw that both men had paused to watch me stumble awkwardly out of view towards my boarding house. The next time was by the Soar Chapel door after the Sunday service. He caught me descending from the balcony on a ladder, my surplice robes billowing about my ankles.

'Better watch or you'll trip up,' he said, beckoning me towards him with a quick sidewards movement of his head. 'God only knows how a little fella like you could move your fingers that fast.' He glanced up to the organ balcony.

'It comes easily, with practice.'

As Uppingham School's only organ scholar, I was obliged to attend both the local Welsh service that our headmaster delivered to the local Methodist congregation, and our own Anglican service. That week I accompanied 'O Come, O Come, Emmanuel' and 'All People That on Earth Do Dwell'.

'I've had my eye on you,' he said, after a pause.

'Why sir?'

'Because you're always on your own.'

My cheeks flushed. The old man noticed.

'It's nothing to be ashamed of. I'm always on my own too. Almost always,' he self-corrected with a grin.

I looked up at the old man talking to me in his close-fitting navy sweater and creased Sunday best. A curtain of white eyebrow hair swooped down across his pale blue eyes, which peered at me with interest.

'What's your name if you don't mind my asking?' I ventured coyly.

'People round here call me Spooner. And you?'

'Robert.'

'Master Robert, that's a promising name.' He paused for a moment or two before continuing: 'Say Robert, do you have any time off?'

'Sometimes on Saturday afternoon before prep.'

'Well come and pay me a visit at my cottage then. It's opposite the slip they use for launching the herring boats. Got the name *Y Wern*.'

The conversation was cut off by the sudden appearance of Evans, my schoolmaster, who peered down his glasses disapprovingly at Spooner and with a pastoral nudge on my shoulder guided me gently back inside.

'And don't forget!' called Spooner back to me, trudging down the mud track that led back to the village through the mire.

Spooner's cottage was small and white on the outside, and cramped and dark on the inside. When I entered, my nose was immediately assaulted by the fetid stench of drying tobacco leaves and the smell of curing meat. Yellowing haunches rotated silently from the crossbeams of the room. Willow baskets of all imaginable dimensions were strung up on the beach stone walls and stacked up in corners along with lobster pots, discarded ropes, drying hops, trays of salted fish and all other imaginable kinds of fishing paraphernalia. Spooner himself was squatting by the peat fire in the inglenook hearth and stoking it with short, incisive jabs.

'So you made it,' he remarked drily. He had removed his hat and I could see that his hair was as white and fleecy as his mariner's beard.

'I'm sorry I'm late.'

'Bah,' he returned with contempt. 'No clocks here.'

I looked around the room and saw he was quite right.

'Bloody clocks and bloody railway,' he continued, clearly irritated by the very thought of them. 'Had no peace in Borth since that railway was built.'

He gestured gruffly to a small three legged stool and a glass of milk prepared for me in front of the fire. I sat down beside him.

'Does anyone know you're here?'

My silence was all the answer he needed.

'Thought as much,' he said with a short laugh and drew a smoking pipe from the breast-pocket of his tunic.

'Did anyone see ya on your way over?'

'None but a group of women dressed in black down by the slip.'

'Know who they are?'

I shook my head.

'In Aberystwyth and other villages in these parts they call them the *Brain y Borth*. The Borth Crows. They're widows whose husbands have perished at sea. Some of them own boats. Some shell cockles, shrimp, even dragnet. Women do all manner of things in Borth. Independent as you like.'

I thought for a moment before asking Spooner a question that had been bothering me for some time.

'How is it you come to speak such good English?'

He coughed, a rasping, racking cough. 'Married an Englishwoman, for my sins.'

'What was her name?'

'Ruth.'

'Did she die?' I asked nervously, following the definitive way he had said it.

'Lord no!' he laughed ruefully. 'Though sometimes I wish she had. She ran away with a railway porter. Don't see much of her anymore. They've gone inland.' Spooner grimaced, his pipe was finished. He cast the remains into the small, orange fire before us. It smelt of moss and cow dung. The old tobacco residue sizzled.

'Weren't you afraid to come today?' he asked, looking at me squarely.

I looked down at my feet. 'I can't deny it.'

'They why did you?'

The old man bent his gaze upon me. His eyebrows bunched together, creating a river of wrinkles on his forehead. The words stuck in my mouth as I struggled to articulate what I had never once admitted to a single of my classmates at Uppingham.

'It's because I saw your boat and because of your occupation. You see, my father, who I never knew, was a fisherman. And his father before that.'

My whole being felt lighter. Spooner clapped his knees at once with satisfaction.

'I knew there was something. I knew it. So the organ scholar is a fisherman's son! Well I never... But you got one thing wrong.'

For the first time that I had known them to, those strange sucking lips of his metamorphosed into a smile. 'I'm not a fisherman.'

'Oh?'

As it turned out, Spooner, or Captain John Hughes as he later introduced himself to me, was a retired sea captain. He had been on sea voyages to Peru, the Horn of Africa and to the spice islands of the Caribbean. He spent the next hour regaling me with stories of Moroccan pirates (who had once come to Borth), of press gangs and mutinees – and nothing could have fired my thirteen-year-old imagination more than the seafaring stories of this old scurvy sea captain which he recited slowly and musically, in his lilting Welsh accent. Seeing my interest piqued and my shyness melting away, he hunched a little closer.

'Would you like to go out with me one day? Nothing tells you who you are like the sea you know.'

I shook my head. 'I can't.'

'Why not?'

'I'm afraid of water. I can't swim.'

'Afraid of water!' The old man laughed. 'What kind of world am I leaving behind to stand watch o'er my earthly remains?'

But he didn't press the point. Instead he got up and led me towards the dingiest corner of the cottage where a large object was covered in rumpled sack cloth.

'Got it off one of the ships. Gave it to Ruth as a wedding present,' he explained, drawing back the sacking to reveal a little white spinet beneath it. 'I like the sound of the thing, but can't make sense of it myself. Would you play something for me?'

At last I knew why Spooner had asked me over to see him. I played 'Abide with Me', since he said he liked it, and other songs from the hymnal. Spooner sat in an old chair beside me, puffing away ponderously at his pipe in such a steady and contented manner that I worried for a moment he would never let me leave.

The next Saturday I saw Spooner on the beach among a general crowd and walked over to join them.

'Good mornin' skipper! How's the piano practice coming on?'

'Very well, thank you Spooner,' I replied, secretly pleased that he had called me "skipper".

'D'ya wanna lend a pair o' hands to bringin' in the catch? Other young 'uns are here to help...' asked Spooner's friend. He had widely spaced wandering eyes and a sock-shaped hat that flopped over one side of his head.

I peered round the hull of the tri-masted fishing boat and saw a number of other young boys my age, gathered barefoot in a small cluster by the surf.

'Go onnn!' cajouled an old woman carrying a full basket of flounders on her back.

'It's something of a local tradition for the youngsters to help bring in the haul – its called *sgadan bys*,' explained Spooner.

I could see a little fishing smack bobbing in the surf. It was drawing closer, the mizzen mast was down and a number of dark figures clustered on the prow, looked out towards the beach.

'Very well.'

I put down my books, rolled up my sleeves, slipped off my shoes and socks and let Spooner introduce me to the other boys in Welsh, after giving me instructions in English.

That afternoon was a revelation to me. The work was harder than I expected: the nets were heavy and wet, the fisherman tired from their long day at sea. The other boys could not speak to me and I could not speak to them. Yet, together, young hands conspired to tug the mighty catch up the beach and towards the fish gutting station where the young women had gathered, ready to gut the herring and load them into carts. Afterwards, trudging back along the beach, my feet pinching with cold and the pockets of my school jacket crammed with slick, slimy herring fish, I realised that I was the happiest I'd been in months. Then and there I resolved to return every Saturday to help the villagers with their work.

Things started to change at school too. Two of the other boys in my form group: Freddy and Thomas, had taken an interest in my Saturday afternoon outings. Under an oath of secrecy, I had taken them out with me to help bring in the haul. When we returned to the boarding house with fistfuls of herring the next day, they were exultant. We found a secret hiding place for them in an old garden shed and cooked them over a beach fire after the Sunday service. It became a ritual of ours, and on Sundays I began to wish the hours at chapel services would hurry on faster so I could meet with Freddy and Thomas and go on our clandestine expedition together. I introduced them to Spooner, who was belligerent and unresponsive, and delighted them both. Then, at long last, just before the end of the herring season, I decided to grant Spooner's long-asked request of me.

We went out alone. I decided not to tell Freddy and Thomas about the plan, feeling instinctively that this was something that needed to happen solely between myself and Spooner. Instead I pleaded sickness with the school matron and then disappeared out through the infirmary window so that we could cast off at the beach in the early morning. Spooner was unusually taciturn with me. His silence felt the more oppressive because though my net-hauling with the other boys had helped deplete my fear of the sea, the reality of being adrift on the unremitting expanse still struck me with panic. I made Spooner promise that we would only go out for an hour and not too far from shore.

He set out the nets and we waited.

'There was a time when you could fish for herring on the beach. They were so bountiful that they would just flow into the nets.' Spooner set his jaw grimly and pulled the low brimmed fishing hat down over his eyes.

Half an hour later and still we had caught nothing in the drift. Every minute seemed to increase Spooner's despondency.

'In this spot, five years ago, the very edges of the boat would be brimming with herring, teeming with herring!'

Sensing his disappointment, I decided to keep quiet.

'The motion making you sick boy?'

He must have seen my nauseous complexion. Unused to being at sea, I felt I could be sick at any moment in the tiny boat.

'Release it boy. That's the best thing to do.'

So I did, from the vessel's starboard.

'Are you afraid?' he asked when I crawled back.

'Yes.' It was an unusually windless day. We were being carried along to Spooner's favourite fishing spot 'The Patches', purely on account of the south-westerly ebbing tide. A dark cloud bank was forming in the North.

'But you came anyway.' He nodded sagely and looked down into the glittering ocean. 'Well done Robert. You've done good.'

Suddenly a shadow passed beneath the boat and a great weight pulled down on my arm.

'Spooner! We've caught something.'

He peered over the edge of the boat.

'By God you're right,' he muttered. 'Could even be a long hundred.'

That was the last time I ever saw Spooner. The school matron soon discovered my disappearance and raised the alarm. One of the boys in the year below who'd caught wind of our activities explained everything. All of the school masters were waiting for me when I got back and I was gated for the remainder of Uppingham school's residence in Borth. Terrible to say, but despite this severe punishment, I almost felt pleased that the tuberculosis epidemic had visited the school premises in Rutland and we'd been forced to evacuate to the countryside. Because of the evacuation I'd met Spooner – one of the greatest and most luminous personalities of my young years – and gone out to sea for the first time. I did go back to Borth again, many years later, when I was working as the chief organist to York Minster. I enquired after Spooner everywhere, but could find no sign of him. *Y Wern* was derelict and boarded up, there were only a dozen fishing smacks left on the spit. In the end one of the old crows told me what happened to him. He had gone out to The Patches last September hunting for herring and was late coming home. The villagers kept a vigil for him on the cliff and lit bonfires on the beach, but he never came back.

Philip Jones

Last Time

The last time I caught the train to Bangor was to meet your family. I had a little MP3 player which I turned like a pebble in my nervous hands. When I arrived I called your dad Mr Thomas, freaking him out and making you laugh. The train hugs the coast.

> The beaches are dabbed
> with dead jellyfish;
> a boy pokes one with a stick.

It's a coincidence that the jellyfish are stranded again, the size of car tyres, deflated twelve years later, floated blind and unthinking on a tide that remembers.

> The mountains watch the train slip by
> one more train, one more tide
> back and forth.

I deliver my well-rehearsed talk at the conference. I eat dinner on my own in a pub overlooking the pier and then sleep in student halls. It's you I think of the whole time, even more so in the morning when Bangor has found its summer bloom.

> Young lovers look into each other's eyes.
> She catches a spider from his hair.

I heard you live up here again but the train pulls away without me having seen you. The tide is in.

A rail line runs parallel
overgrown with shrubs
and dandelions.

Rebecca Lawn

The Mountains

Adela added a few more thoughts to her list and then tucked her notebook away in a kitchen drawer. The oil was hot enough now – she could begin deep-frying the gogoşi. She dropped the doughy balls one by one into the pan.

Her family were sitting around the large oak table in the next room. She glanced through the doorway at Cristian. Nothing worried her more than her grandson. Of course, they all worried her in their own way: her son and granddaughter, too. She sometimes wondered whether the lines etched deep onto her face were not in fact the family tree. If so, Cristian was the line that ran from the inner corner of her eye and cut across her face, the path of a tear.

Oh, that boy. Her thought was almost spoken as she took out the last few sweet pastries and laid them on the side. The pan spat a few specks of oil onto her black headscarf. Adela wiped them off with her hand, her fingers tucking in a defiant curl while there.

She shook her head. How could two siblings be so different? Cristian was thin. And quiet. No, quiet was too small a word. You had to keep reminding yourself he was even there. With Roxana, you had to remind yourself that you were still there; her body and voice took up the room. But Cristian was swallowed up by everything around him. What would happen to him?

Would he not just disappear?

Adela kept an eye on him as he picked at a stuffed cabbage roll. Each bite seemed to stay in his mouth a long time. He was chewing too slowly.

'Eat, Cristian,' she said. 'Remember, when the winter sets in, and it always comes sooner than you think, you'll be glad of those extra kilos. No one ever died from being too fat.'

'Yes, Grandma,' Cristian said.

'Actually,' Roxana began, tearing off a piece of bread and dipping it into some pickle, 'I saw a documentary on TV where this American man weighed a half ton and they had to airlift him out of...'

'No, no,' Adela said, and then, on second thought, conceded: 'America is a strange place. Perhaps it can happen there. But in Romania? No. Not possible.'

Roxana shrugged. Sergiu winked at her, whispered 'good to know', and cut himself a thick slice of sheep's cheese.

'Cristian, have some while they're hot. I'll roll one in sugar for you. Here.'

Adela held out her hand.

Cristian made his way to his grandmother, squished the soft, doughy ball between his fingers and took a tentative bite.

'You used to love these!' Adela said, resisting the urge to pinch his cheek. He was the youngest but she mustn't forget that he was nineteen now, a man, a student at Babeş-Bolyai University. And anyway, his cheeks were so gaunt there would be nothing to grip onto.

The odd thing was, he had been such a chubby baby. The cheeks on him! He had been stockier than Roxana, despite the three years between them. Andrei joked that he would be a wrestler. He used to hold the baby's little arms and put them up ready for a pretend fight. They gave him vegetables from the garden, milk, a little bit of meat, now and then, when they could, and grapes, too, how he loved those, just like his grandfather. Cristian was their little light. They thanked the Lord every day for him.

'How was your journey here, Cristian?' She asked, eager to stretch out their time together before he sat back down at the table.

'Fine,' he said.

'And are you studying hard?'

'I'm trying. It's very difficult.'

'Keep working hard and you will succeed.'

Cristian pushed his hands into the pockets of his jeans and bit his lip.

'Do you like coming here?'

He nodded. 'I always like to see you, to make sure you're well, and to see the mountains and pick the grapes and breathe the air here.'

Adela thought perhaps this would be a life he preferred to his own, but village life was fragile. A single element could knock it off balance, and the people here knew this. They could trust neither that the highs would last nor that the lows would end; nature was too capricious. Her neighbours were not unhappy, but they were tired. It was in their worn, sun-beaten faces, in how their backs hunched, in how fathers and sometimes mothers too had no choice but to leave their children to find work abroad. But Cristian was too young to see any of that. And besides, she could not let him waste his education.

'The good thing is, these mountains, they're not going anywhere,' Adela said.

Cristian smiled and took another sweet pastry.

'You know,' Adela began, 'during the worst years, well before you were born, when we were scared and thin, just knowing those mountains were here, seeing them bring colour...'

Her voice drifted off. It surprised her how memories could still surface like that. She cleared her throat and smoothed down her dress.

From the expression on his face, Adela could tell that she had worried her grandson. They had been born into two different Romanias, and she wanted him to concern himself only with the future.

'You know, it's funny, even your dad was thin then! Imagine that!' she said, forcing a smile.

She looked over at Sergiu, who hadn't heard. He was helping himself to some more sausages. His navy-blue shirt was stretched over his belly, lending a sheen to the fabric; and his face was pink from the plum liquor. He had recently bought a step machine to lose the extra kilos, but Adela liked that he was a good size.

'Grandma, do you think it's time?' Roxana called over.

'Are you going to do it?' Adela replied, lifting her eyebrows. 'Do you have the strength?'

'The women in this family have all the strength!' Roxana laughed.

It was an ongoing joke between the two of them. Adela had always had a soft spot for Roxana, her outspoken, auburn-haired granddaughter. The child had got the best of her late mother and the best of her father. And there was a little bit of herself in her, too, a female strength, a quiet confidence. Men may lift and throw, but women can withstand.

Roxana didn't think she needed a husband. But she could do with one. It was all very well that she had a good job in Cluj Napoca, working as a teacher, but what was that without a husband by your side, someone to share the memories with? Adela was not of the old ways. She had always prided herself on being an equal. Equal but different, perhaps, but inferior to no one. Andrei knew what he was getting into. He could have picked Florina, the timid, head-bowing type who brought round sweet pastries even after their engagement was announced. But he didn't.

So, she would remember to add to her list, to tell Roxana: you don't need a husband to be whole, you don't need a husband because you can't survive alone. But how wonderful it is to have someone to go through life with. The joys are lifted; the sorrows tempered.

Every day she missed Andrei. He had annoyed her more than any other living soul; their conversations towards the end were just the same small grievances over and over, muttered under their breath. But oh, how she missed him! If he were here now, what would he say? Ha, maybe he wouldn't say anything, his mouth would be so full! But maybe this once she would let him talk with his mouth full. She could let it pass.

Adela imagined him, then, at her age, an age she never thought she would get to, especially alone. There he was next to his son and his grandchildren. He listened to their conversation, all the while tracing some of the grooves in the table with his fingers, checking that the wood had not cracked. He had on his grey shirt, and white tufts of hair peeked out from underneath his brown cap. As usual, he had brought in half the field on his shoes.

She took a deep breath. He would always be in the oak table that he had carved, the centre of the room. And she felt him as the draft of cool air that came in with her when she closed the door to the outside. She looked at her family and smiled sadly.

'Come on, Grandma!' Roxana said. 'Away from the oven with you!'

Adela broke from her reverie. Roxana folded her grandmother's arm around hers and led her out towards the two large wooden barrels, filled with the day's pickings.

A sugary scent wafted in the air. To the right, behind several farmhouses, the white dome of a church poked into the sky. Across from them were the grand Carpathian Mountains, patched in red and orange and yellow like a quilt. It was a view Adela had seen for a lifetime, but could never tire of, even if the Lord granted her another. Each time she came out she was sure that there before her laid His finest work. Sergiu said she thought that because she had not seen Italy or Germany, France or Spain. But she did not need to.

'Now, let's see what these women can do,' Roxana said, scraping her long hair back. She rolled up the ends of her jeans and washed her feet at the outside tap before climbing into one of the barrels. As she moved her feet over the grapes, loosening their skins, the sweet scent grew stronger.

Sergiu ferreted around Adela, urging her to use her walking stick for support. She wafted him away. She could stand just fine. Her mind drifted to the letter underneath her notebook in the kitchen drawer. She had not long ago received the diagnosis from the doctor: the same unforgiving illness that had taken Andrei. She would withstand it for as long as she could, tell no one. All she needed was enough time to help each of them along their paths a little more before she left them.

Adela was not yet sure what to write in her notebook

for her only son; perhaps that he needed to see what he had, appreciate it more. Except for the mountains it was all too temporary. Adela held herself still, willing her feet to be heavy. She thought of them as having roots like trees, grounding her.

James Lloyd

The Flood

The first droplet
bleeds like dye
before it begins.

A torrential shower
shatters on the cobblestones
As the crowd disperses

for shelter, hiding
in shops and restaurant
doorways, a crush of people

in the entrance to the church.
Shoulder to shoulder
they watch the rain

glug from drains into
the street, like a lock
set to fill, or a platform

between two trains
anticipating the rush
of people waiting for

the signal. The
shower thins.
Wet eyes look up

past dripping gutters
and fish scale rooftops
to an emptied sky

and the crowd
gushes out
into the street.

The After

Slate slabs read
like welsh words
to them.

They were
masters of discarding
the imperfect.

    Now
ferns flourish
between the lines
of their work.

They are remembered
for the void

and the mountains
        upon mountains
of the unused.

Eddie Matthews

The Everyman

On November 24, 1971, a man disappeared from a flight with $200,000 ransom. He was never found.

FBI Records Vault – D.B. Cooper Part 08 of 22: Page 2

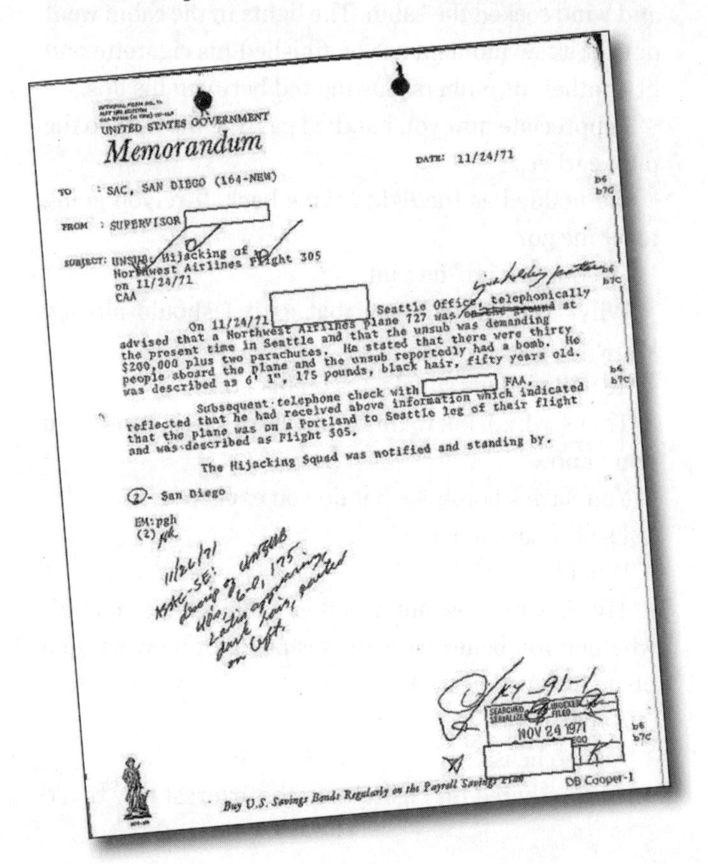

UNITED STATES GOVERNMENT

Memorandum

DATE: 11/24/71

TO : SAC, SAN DIEGO (164-NEW)

FROM : SUPERVISOR [redacted]

SUBJECT: UNSUB; Hijacking of Northwest Airlines Flight 305 on 11/24/71 CAA

On 11/24/71 [redacted] Seattle Office, telephonically advised that a Northwest Airlines plane 727 was on the ground at the present time in Seattle and that the unsub was demanding $200,000 plus two parachutes. He stated that there were thirty people aboard the plane and the unsub reportedly had a bomb. He was described as 6' 1", 175 pounds, black hair, fifty years old.

Subsequent telephone check with [redacted] FAA, reflected that he had received above information which indicated that the plane was on a Portland to Seattle leg of their flight and was described as Flight 305.

The Hijacking Squad was notified and standing by.

2 - San Diego

EM:pgh
(2)

SEARCHED ... INDEXED ... SERIALIZED ... FILED ...
NOV 24 1971

b6 b7C

DB Cooper-1

Buy U.S. Savings Bonds Regularly on the Payroll Savings Plan

November 24, 1971: Washington

He sat in the middle of the last row of the empty 727 smoking a Raleigh filter-tip cigarette. His black attaché case was half-open with eight red sticks pointing out – a wire combining the sticks into a single strand which he held beside a canvas bag full of rubber-banded wads of $20s. When the hijacker instructed the passengers to de-plane in Seattle 45 minutes prior, he required one stewardess to stay on, then negotiated a flight plan to Mexico City. She sat beside the case, inhaling his smoke while rain pelleted the windows like Kalashnikov fire, and wind rocked the cabin. The lights in the cabin went out for a few moments as he finished his cigarette and lit another, its embers glowing red between his lips.

'I appreciate how you handled passing the note to the pilot earlier.'

She nodded as the lights came back. 'Are you going to let me go?'

'Of course I am,' he said.

'Why? Why do you say that as if I should already know?'

He adjusted his sunglasses on his nose.

'That's why I knew this would work – because you don't know.'

'You have a bomb – what do you expect?'

'I said I have a bomb.'

'What?'

'The question is not whether you believe me. It's whether you believe a man is capable of blowing up a plane to get some cash.'

'A man – yes.'

'And so he is.'

He smothered his cigarette in the armrest tray that'd

filled with ash like a volcanic crater. She saw a rash on his neck. Or was it a burn? He handed her the wire while he flicked the spark wheel of the lighter to ignite his new cigarette. The case was opened toward her on the seat, red sticks in two rows nestled in the velvet interior like a set of steak knives. He blew the smoke into the aisle, then offered the cigarette to the stewardess who hesitated, then took it. Her impulse – a touch of the cigarette to the wire... oblivion... or bullshit. She handed the wire back to him and blew smoke across the seats in front of her and coughed. She regained her breath and took off her stewardess hat, letting her dark red hair fall to her shoulders while her tapping foot keeled on the navy blue carpet. She passed him the cigarette and he noticed her twisting her engagement ring.

'You still set on that engagement?' he said.

She looked at the bronze band of the ring and its composite stone. 'Why wouldn't I be?'

'You're a stewardess. Your job means being away. Something tells me you didn't choose this profession – or volunteer to stay on this plane – by accident.'

'I don't know why I did.'

'In my experience, this altitude allows you a certain clarity you can't get anywhere else.'

November 24, 2011: Umpqua River, Oregon

A father told his son the skyjacking story while sitting across a campfire.

'They ever find the body?' Cade, the second born, said.

'I don't know,' the father said.

The fire glowed on a dirt patch on the riverbank and crickets trilled from the wooded hill on the other side.

The bark of coyotes echoed down-river until a gunshot silenced them; Cade straightened his back against the synthetic folding chair, pulling his sleeves down to cover his eczema. The denim jacket he wore, borrowed from his father, was a size too big.

'How old were you in 1971?'

'Let's see... I would have been... same age as you – 21.'

'I'm 23.'

'I said about.'

'No you didn't.'

Cade spat and watched the saliva bubble in the flames while his father yawned.

The fire sounded like flags in a wind tunnel.

'Was it all over the news?'

'It was covered on local news in San Diego where I lived at the time.'

'Were you living alone?'

'That question came out of nowhere,' the father said.

Cade shrugged. His father picked up a stick and shifted the coals at the bottom of the fire then put the stick back in the dirt and looked at his son, whose hands shook as he held them out the fire. They listened to owls call each other from either side of the river, firelight moving on the water like an apparition.

'Aren't you more curious about what happened to Cooper?' the father said.

'Now I'm curious about a period of your life you've never talked about before.'

'It's not important.'

'You always say that. Maybe it's important to me, Dad.'

'It shouldn't be.'

'You used to tell me that you wouldn't lie to me. I remember asking you questions that you should have lied to me about, like if you thought I was smart, and you still told the truth.'

'That applies to anything in your life. You're my son. To you, my life started when you were born.'

'Why'd you bring up a story from 1971 then?'

'I didn't know what else to talk about.'

The father untwisted the cap of his Diet Pepsi and finished it, then tossed the plastic bottle into the fire and watched it melt, collapsing in on itself. Cade got up and walked toward the river.

'Where you going?'

'To take a leak.'

He walked around a corner until hidden from sight. His boots made little splashes in the mud and he slipped, landing on his back and he stayed down on the grass of the slope, looking at the stars that sat just above the jagged horizon made so by pine trees. He watched his breath plume the air and clasped his hands in front of him. After 15 minutes passed, he wiped mud off his hands on the grass and walked back to the fire and saw his father hadn't moved.

'Why did we even come out here today?' Cade said, taking his seat.

'To spend father-son time. It's what you do.'

'You don't have to talk about it like it's paying taxes.'

'Like what?'

'An obligation,' Cade said.

'You're so full of it. What makes you think I don't like spending time with you?'

'I don't know, might have to do with the fact that you keep looking at me across the fire like I'm a fuck-up.'

'You look at yourself that way.'

'Don't you?'

His father leaned forward and stared at his son, lips

thin. His eyes creased like a poker champion dealt a bad hand, while Cade circled the mud with the toe of his boot, knocking over his empty Coors Light bottle. His father turned over the contents within his sheepskin coat pocket.

'I was living with my fiancée at the time.'

'What are you talking about?'

'Pay attention, Son. You asked me if I was living alone.'

'I... never knew you were engaged before Mom.'

'My fiancée was working on the plane Cooper hijacked.'

He passed her the cigarette. She let the ashes fall to the same carpet where she'd picked up nail clippings, peanuts, and wadded-up receipts on her hands and knees 12 hours before. He stretched his legs and slicked his balding dark hair back with his hand then looked at his watch.

'Take me to the rear passenger door, please.'

She got up slowly and brushed some of the cigarette ash off her uniform skirt and walked one row up to cross to the other aisle, then escorted him to the door 15-feet behind them.

'Show me how to open it.'

'You pull this lever toward you, then turn the handle 180 degrees and push out.'

'Okay. Go to first class and close the curtain behind you.'

She stood there and looked at him, sweat beaded his forehead above his black sunglasses. She turned and walked, getting halfway up the aisle.

'Wait - come back.'

She saw bundles of $20s spill onto the floor.

'The zipper broke. I need you to go to the row up there and cut up the extra parachute and retie the money so it's secure.'

'I don't have a knife.'

'Here.'

She walked back to him and he handed her a collapsible hunting knife with a Latin engraving on the cedarwood handle. She walked to the parachute, took it in her hands and cut through the outer lining, hacking off a length of suspension line to use as string, and unfurled the parachute in the aisle three rows in front of him. She found a small, detached section of the nylon canopy.

'That's the pilot chute, cut that off and wrap it in that,' he said. She nodded and cut, then walked to where he sat cross-legged on the floor to get the money. The lights flickered and he held up a wad of cash as she knelt, her nose a foot from his, blade in hand.

'For you.'

'Why are you doing this?'

'I thought you deserved a cut of the pie. You have beautiful amber eyes, after all.'

'Not that. *This*. All this: the bomb, the money.'

He put the cash down. She looked at him and waited but he didn't speak or move, so she dragged the bag along the carpet by the strap to where she left the pilot chute. She kept the money in the canvas bag and folded the chute over it on all sides, then bound it in suspension line four times over, knotting it. She towed the makeshift bag back down the aisle by the knot she made and he looked up at her.

'I was faithful to my wife when she wasn't to me. Loved my son when he didn't love me. Served my country when it didn't serve me. I wanted to see what it felt like to let it all go.'

She nodded, 'you know I think you're capable of the reverse as well.'

He squinted.

'Earlier, you asked me if I thought a man was capable of blowing up a plane for money. I said yes. But I think a man is capable of the opposite too – a good deed of the same magnitude as the destruction in that briefcase. Each man to his own ability.'

She walked down the aisle toward the front of the plane and closed the curtains of first-class, waited a few seconds, then parted them – enough for one eye to see through – and saw him facing the passenger door, praying on his knees.

The Milky Way shown above like a bag of salt poured on wet pavement, while lights on waterfront houses glowed across the field east of them.

'So she, she, told you this story *first-hand?*'

'She called me from Reno where they refuelled after he jumped to tell me she was breaking off our engagement.'

'I can't believe this. Wait, so, did she ever tell you why she was breaking it off?'

'She mailed this to me with the ring.' He tossed his son a hunting knife with a cedarwood handle. Cade looked at it in the firelight – the Latin phrase on it said *Actiones secundum fidei*.

'It was his,' the father said.

'What does it mean?'

'Action follows belief.'

His father sat still. Deep wrinkles that bisected his cheekbones shone in the firelight and his eyebrows arched in a way Cade hadn't seen since primary school.

The wind picked up and flowed through the grove of pines by the road's edge, making the branches sway like parents on a dance floor.

'She didn't have to turn this into the FBI as evidence?'

His father shrugged, eyes unmoved from the fire.

'You carry this around?'

He nodded.

At a bench in the car park above the river sat an old man resting his knees. He watched the father and son below as he exhaled smoke from his cigarette that warmed his chest. He massaged his arthritic knee, blood flowing back to it as a few minutes passed. He looked across the street to the pine grove that rose through mist, hand trembling on the bench as he lifted himself from it. He stamped out his cigarette on the bench and limped toward the pines, boots crunching the sticks that'd fallen on the wet street. A man of the Umpqua put his arm around the old man on the other side and they walked together into the pines through a herd of sleeping elk, running their hands over the tips of their ears as the fog rolled onto the road.

Eve Elizabeth Moriarty

Borderline

Since diagnosis,
nothing about me is my own.
Every argument is a *split*,
every extra slice a *binge*.
I am learning that there are words for everything
I do, or think, new ones sterile with DSM detachment.
I am a walking catalogue
of symptoms and faults.

When I can't sleep (*insomnia*) I think:
This is how those girls in crinolines
must have felt, in the hysteria days.
(*Projection*)
Afraid to show emotion
for fear of the asylum,
any passion a sign of something dark.

I thought I would feel free
when I knew what was wrong, how
to help it, but the world *borderline* has trapped me.
My impulsivity is predictable.
I have become both dangerous
and pitiable,
An NHS leaflet, a self-help book, a website
dedicated to not dating *girls like me.*

At night I dream of blister-packs and worksheets,
hypnosis tapes. The sleek interface of the app I use
to track my flaws swims in my mind's eye
as I twist, restless, sweaty with meds,
wrapped in words my psychiatrist lends me.

Michael Muia

Young Tommy

(Second Prize, Fiction)

'Stand to, stand to!' comes the growling whisper of the sergeant as he hurries along the line. I know it's still dark as my eyes remain closed, a knot of dread involuntarily grips my insides. My body knows what today holds.

I hear the groan and hushed protest as men and boys from my pals battalion return from their broken slumber, trying to eke out the final warm embrace with loved ones. Dreams so vivid and real they conquer this nightmare we have found ourselves in.

I can feel my body protest the day; aching leg muscles and shoulders have become a normal feeling. What heaven it will be. I reach down and feel the familiar touch of a walnut stock. Zeus's Thunder is the name I've given my Lee Enfield rifle, deadly in my hands. My forefinger finds the tally score I've etched into the butt. I caress it – thirty-six – I don't need to count them. My sodden 1902 pattern service dress is heavy and the thick woollen material clings to my body like a parasite clinging to a host. It resists me as I sit up onto my elbows.

'My lord, my elbows hurt too,' I mutter to myself as I lean back and rest against the mud walls I've carved out of this trench to make my bed space. The dense, clay-bound mud of northern France is unforgiving and saps the energy out of the most robust individual. I've dug a lot here.

I hear quick footsteps splashing up the trench; the returning sergeant glances in at me.

'Come on, George boy, fifteen minutes 'till go time.'

'Aye sarnt, I'm moving,' I say, swinging my legs out of my earthly coffin and poking my head out. I glance down and see the rippling blackness shimmer in the dying moonlight,

'It's risen again,' I say to nobody listening. I flick my gaze along the trench, looking left and right as I stretch the tightness out of my neck. I can see movement, men emerging from their 'graves' in various states of dress. Some are stretching and some just sit and ponder like they are fishing on the riverbank with not a care in the world. If only we were fishing. It reminds me of a story I've heard of the dead coming back to life and climbing out of their tombs ravenous for living flesh. I know some men won't be rising today. Not two days have passed since we lost Pat Mcgavie, and Cyril 'Two times', a foul-mouthed young'un, we gave him the moniker Two Times by his insistence on saying everything twice.

'Hey up old man, old man,' he would say to me.

'Hey up yourself! Old man? I'm only old enough to be your brother laddie!' I would reply.

'Not likely... likely!' he would laugh. He and Pat got into a commotion over a tin of bully beef; in the exchange both men stood up, silhouetting themselves above the safety of the trench. The crack of the round could be heard after Pat's body had crumpled to the ground. Cyril frozen by shock, stood stock still like an ancient oak tree in a forest, as the Hun cycled his rifle, reloaded and sent Cyril on his way to join the back of the queue for his meeting with Saint Peter. We were told a few hours later that Cyril was only fourteen. Maybe I was old enough to be his father.

A noise snaps me back into the moment – a young Tommy, I think his name is Jim. A battlefield replacement, still wet behind the ears. Yet to be tested over here, his kit still fresh and unblemished, unaware of the horrors over yonder. I look at him and see that he's unsure of what to do. Grabbing my webbing and bandoliers and slinging Zeus's Thunder over my arm like I'm an aristocrat about to shoot a defenceless pheasant out of the sky, I move closer to him. I notice he is trembling.

'Jim, isn't it?' I ask.

'J... J... James,' he blurts.

'All right Jim, charge that rifle, grab some three-o-three's if you need 'um, bring that bayonet and don't forget to drink some water,' I tell him from experience

I see him fumble in his bandolier for some rounds to fill his magazine. His hands are shaking. I reach out and the grab the rifle. He holds onto it and pulls it towards me, bringing him with it. His grip relents and his eyes lock with mine. His eyes are bloodshot, he's been crying.

'Don't you worry, my lad, not nothin' to worry about,' I confidently lie. I tell myself this same thing over and over, like a Buddhist chanting the *Tiratana*, a mantra I've been reciting since Ypres in 1914. I grab a handful of rounds and skilfully load the magazine, not taking my eyes away from the young Tommy. I can tell this impresses him.

'You been over the top before my lad?'

'N... No, I only got here 4 days ago'. He looks sheepish as he thinks I don't recall. I do recall. I've given up getting to know anybody else; I have grieved over friends these past two years, more than many a man would grieve in a thousand lifetimes.

'I know lad, stick with me and we won't go far wrong. Do as I do, and you'll see tomorrow,' I lie again.

Men begin to make their way towards the junction of the communication trench. I wonder if the Huns know we're coming today. If they don't, they soon will.

'Come on Jim boy! Time to go,' I say, handing his rifle back to him. I turn and move off towards the junction, slipping on my webbing like a favourite jacket and instinctively reaching for the pouches and checking the clasps are fixed in place. I hear him follow on; glancing back I see him doing the same. Do as I do, that's what I'd told him.

Hunger pangs my stomach. No breakfast for us today, I've got a tin of bully beef left that will do nicely for lunch, I reassure myself.

We approach the other men; apart from the splashing of the water under foot there is no sound. We all know what we've got to do.

'You ready George boy?' I hear coming from over my shoulder. I spin around and start to walk backwards, recognising the familiar voice.

'Good day for it don't you reckon Ed?' I have known Edward Shimble since late 1914. A ferocious man who was a docker before the war. A short, stocky guy with jet black hair and eyes as blue as the base of a flame and arms so thick they look like the barrel of an artillery gun. Ed is a stalwart of this battalion and an example to all of us of how we should be, unyielding and uncompromising in the face of the enemy.

'Always a good day to thump fritz!' he says, his blue eyes dancing with anticipation. Not a flicker of apprehension. I turn back around, glancing at the young Tommy as I do so. He's still on my coat tails, a good sign.

We splash our way along the communication trench that connects the rear of the line to the front. The mass of men slows its pace as we reach the frontline. The air changes here. I notice the sun heaving its glow towards the horizon – not long to go now. I know the pace will quicken shortly and before we can think about it we will be in the action. I know that if we linger here longer than necessary the men's courage will begin to waiver. I've seen it happen before. I hit the junction, turn left and know the ladder I need to get to. I catch the whiff of putrefaction, merging as a ball in the back of my throat. I resist the urge to gag, but the young Tommy can't help it. I hear him wretch and lace the ground with last night's rations.

'Dew, get it up Jim lad! We've all done it.'

I know he won't be the only one vomiting – even the battle hardened are susceptible. I pass several ladders with men perched half way up; they have canvas hoods that cover their heads and drape across their soldiers. Periscopes stick out of the top; it's too dangerous to expose yourself above the parapet, just ask Pat and Cyril. I tap the sentry's boot to let him know I'm passing him. A trick we'd learnt along the way, it keeps a man from getting tunnel vision and going crazy looking across the seventy-five yards of hell that spans the gap between us and the Huns.

My mind flicks to the enemy, who've been here for years. The Kaiser and his generals anticipated the movement of the Allies long before the Allies themselves. Beaumont-Hamel, nestled along the River Somme, is where we find ourselves. Fritz knows this place well and has prepared accordingly; their trenches are deep and strong with sandbags and machine guns along a fifteen-mile stretch. This is a trench system that is decisively dangerous, strewn with snipers and barbed wire that coils out into no mans land like a deadly snake waiting to sink its venomous fangs into an unsuspecting prey. I check my rear pouch for the reassuring touch of the steel wire cutters.

I reach my ladder. I know I only have a few minutes before the action begins. I pull out my canteen, glug my water and look up to the breaking day. I don't dwell on home for now is not the time. Jim has stopped behind me, he's digging around for his canteen. Good boy.

'It's going to be quick lad,' I tell him as men shuffle past, some making eye contact and others away in their thoughts. It's not a time for sentiment but Ed grips my shoulder as he draws near.

'I'll see you over there in a bit, Georgie boy.'

'Aye no bother lad,' I return. I watch him settle against the ladder twenty yards from me.

I hear a distant deep booming sound like a bass drum beating the rhythm for marching troops; I know what it is. I grip the young Tommy and pull him in so close that my lips are nearly touching his ear.

'Stay close to me, don't stop and never run in a straight line,' I tell him, the sense of urgency in my voice hammering home the reality that we're about to go over the top. I notice the Sergeant pacing the line, his arm by his side. I notice the barrel of his revolver. I see the hammer cocked back, reminding the meek amongst us of our duty.

'And whatever you do, don't stay he...'

The noise of the artillery round travelling through the air drowns out my words. It sounds like a steam train rushing past my ear; the rounds are the size of a man and twice as heavy, and thud into the area in front of us. The explosion sucks the oxygen out of my body and makes my eyes shake in their sockets, like a cheap baby's rattle. Above the force of the increasing cadence of the life-sapping explosions I can feel the young Tommy tremble. Don't linger here, lad.

I unsling my rifle, work the action of the bolt and chamber a round. I kiss Zeus's Thunder, and begin to creep up the ladder. The young Tommy remains stock still with shoulders hunched over. I kick him like I would a stubborn Shire. He snaps back to his reality and looks at me, eyes crazed with fear. He's mouthing something, but I can't make it out. The deafening crescendo of explosions has been replaced by the sound of wet fingers dragging along a pane of glass; this I know, is the sound dying men make. It's working. I know it's time, the explosions stop, and I hear the faint blast of an officer's whistle. Time to go. I kick hard up the ladder and roll over the breach of the trench. I don't check to see if Jim is following me, too late to worry about that.

I regain my feet and move quickly, my putties slopping through the dense clay. I bend at the waist and keep my head up. I see the mist of the artillery barrage move silently in front of me. The sun has betrayed us. I can see through the mist to the Huns' heads moving quickly from left to right in their trench across the churned, cratered sanctum of no man's land, where men go and never return. They're not all dead. I hear the rounds buzzing passed me like a swarm of angry bees. I hope that young Tommy hasn't done what I've done.

Nathan Munday

Mount Keen[1]

Why should I care for a dying hare,
whose breath is spent on a lonely hill?

A quiet land. A sudden end.
I opened this purple book. grouse
I turned a page and felt it bend grouse
with heather, moss, and brooks.

grouse
The path was fractured by the grouse.

We watched like gods, and let them flee,
the water-fall parts, and lets them loose,
but its flood enveloped me.

mountain
We came to the place— that Keen,
Angus's cone-shaped hill.
We caught a sight. Perhaps a cairn?
The wind began to kill.

The sky was clear.
The stone was near.
It split like two, long ears.

The hare was guardian of this cairn,
a grass-hopper – beached for years.
The Roman shores were distant tarns,

1 Mount Keen is the most eastern Munro in Scotland.

but this bare land:
a rock-pool lair
or chair for Scottish clans.

The Munro ticked, both book and leg, so we began to flee.

Victoria's well was in the vale,
A space for sleeping lords.
I gazed towards the eerie wail
and heard her praying chords.

A saintly woman bowed in prayer,
Melangell on the hill;[2]
the beating hearts of leaping hares
had found their solace still.

And then, this hare
with drumming heart
and hurting eyes;
Its red legs marked,
and fainting sighs.

The saint was nowhere to be seen.

Ptolemy had seen a cosmic hunt:
Orion with his hounds.
Major, minor – canister shot,
I heard the distant sounds.

'Lepus', I asked the dying thing,
'Did you pursue the stars?'
His eyes contracted to a ring
His body was so marred.

---

2 Melangell was a Celtic Saint.

I tried my best to warm him still,
but by the time I touched his skin,
His eyes were milky

Dim

Mer de Glace[3]

A shrinking tongue licks
the valley white.

A skier snakes down the glacier like
a catamaran on a choppy sea.

The deep snow foams at his straining heels.

A poem scribed – his poles pen ink.
The paper scarred with catastrophic lines.
Every turn becomes a sentence.

He finishes the Mer de Glace. He turns back
like a statue. The story looks like a pair of serpents
dangling from a jagged horizon.

It started with a fall – two children
skied through this alabaster garden.
Both he and she should have known better.
He wondered whether the Mer remembered her
or had kept her like a butterfly, trapped in ice.
She rolled in an avalanche and died.

But he survived and skis the glassy sea
like Adam searching for Eve

---

3 The glacier above Chamonix-Mont-Blanc.

Tylluan

(Commended)

Truan i'r dylluan deg
Ar ddistial na rydd osteg

What a shame that the fair owl
Will not be silent on its branch

– Dafydd ap Gwilym

He was standing in the middle of the road. My parents saw him. It was near Abraham's Bridge but before McDonald's roundabout.

We were in our car and it wasn't even night time. But it was just there. Mam was wooed by it, so she clicked her indicator down and turned the steering wheel like a captain on a bridge.

Our vessel rolled on the hard shoulder. I watched as Dad opened the door. His legs landed on the dry tarmac and his arms folded back like a hieroglyph. His right eye shone in the sun and his grey crest blew in the wind – but I remained in the nest.

The trees watched as Mam ran towards the hooded nun. She wrapped a blanket around him. He didn't stir. Hoo-di-hoo seemed a sad memory – a ghoulish bird. His body was completely still except for its garments that moved in the breeze. His feather life was old whilst his glassy eyes were bold and tired.

Tenderly, they picked him up in a blanket and brought him to the car; he didn't cry or struggle. They kept a gap in the cowl for him to see. I caught a glimpse of his wide eyes. I stared into them like water, conscious that his cross was now the flightless air, and his talons – three forward, one back – were the nails that bound him to it.

I had a distant memory of seeing a barn owl as a toddler. My parents were there. They took me to that lonely church called Soar-y-Mynydd. My mother knelt beside me and pointed her beautiful index towards the window. And in that window, the white presence of a barn owl was incarnated on my mind. I was afraid and hid in my mother's coat. Soar was such a brittle place and its resident became a relic in my mind...

We drove home. I told Mam to drive carefully. She was carrying such a precious load. The road had already massacred his brothers and sisters, the stinking badger on the sideway and the fox flying to his doom.

We arrived safety. This *Llan* was an enclosure; ancient in its making – a precious station. My parents got out of the car before showing me the owl.

Dad took my hand:

'Feel his feathers... They're soft.'

'I'm afraid...'

'No, he is tender but tired,' Dad re-assured me. 'Go on... it's easy'.

I stretched out my hand and felt that feather life. Mam smiled and pointed out its beak, its beautiful colours, and its eyes. She described his browns and whites but then went on and revealed oranges and blacks hidden between the shades. There was a mystery about his perfection.

We took him into the garage so he could recover. Mam gathered some moss to guard him from the cruel wind. Smaller creatures had to share their space now.

The moon was purple. The mountain was gloomy

in the distance. The earth was straining to contain its worry. Dad realised that its wing was hurting, so he stayed there for a while.

I went to bed.

*

The morning was the voice of someone not spoken for a long time. There was a smile in Dad's words:

'Son... I think he'll fly today'.

We weren't too far from where we found him and the sun made the owl restless – some *hiraeth* for some hidden arbour.

I remember thinking what a strange home for an owl. Why did she choose a church to live in? She should have been free. She should have been in the trees and in the valley. She should have been hunting all night and sleeping through the day. But instead, she was locked in that ancient site like a Celtic somnambulist. Perhaps it was the flower maiden, or Arianrhod, or the coileach-oidhche, crowing from the past.[4]

Where was his tree I wonder? Perhaps he was hungry. I became more and more familiar with him as the day went on. I wandered into the garage and sat at his feet. I told him about my conkers and soldiers. I listened to his subtle flecks of breath. The sudden movement of his wing was terrifying, but I stayed and loved him.

There are days that are so still that you can hear the animals calling. It was one of those days and I stayed in that presence for hours.

I tried to give him milk but he warned me with those eyes. I was unwise. I tried to touch him again, like I had done the previous night, but it wasn't possible. He

---

4 Blodeuwedd was the flower maiden transformed into an owl in the *Mabinogi*. Arianrhod is the Celtic Moon Goddess and Coileach-oidhche is the Gaelic for Night-Cockerel.

moved away and squealed like Lechuza.[5]

Dad came in:

'He's wild son. He's awake and restless... I think he wants to go home'.

'Isn't this his new home, Dad?'

'No. He's our guest but he has to go back. He's got his own home which is high and distant.'

Dad pointed at the trees and I saddened at the prospect of the owl's goodbye. Dad had a blanket in his hand. He bowed down like a wise man, picking the load in his palms. The bird left some white marks on the floor. He even left a feather. I grabbed it, afraid that someone would see. Dad carried him into the garden.

'Dad, he's afraid...' I shouted, '...please, let him stay!'

'His time has come. We have to let him go'.

'But Dad! He belongs to us!' I begged.

I was upset. I thought about the higher views and the green leaves that would hide him from us. His home was unfamiliar. I had never been to the highest trees. I had climbed the limes behind our home and had wandered through the firs and pines. I imagined an ancient oak tree – too sacred to climb. He would be peaceful there – the only disturbance being a squirrel or the wind might tread its branches on a heavy night.

I left him in the garden. I couldn't bear to see him fly.

*

'Come on cariad, let's go and see tylluan'.

Mam took me by the hand and we stood together in the porch.

Dad placed the owl on the patio. He was facing the right way. At the front of our house was a dangerous road but at the back of our house was the woodland. My father looked at my mother and stepped away from tylluan ...

---

5 She was a Mexican witch that could change into an owl.

The owl turned his head to the left and to the right
Its wings unfolded wide.
flew
Stretching across the patio, flew
lifting off, it flew flew flew
away. We were happy.
But then the owl moved in a circle.
'Dad. No!'
'*Paid poeni cariad*,' my mother looked at my father. My father ran to the front garden.

We followed.

I didn't understand. I never understood why the owl flew towards the road. His talons grabbed the tarmac; his wings were stretched out wide; his eyes looked back, and power struck him like the earth did, so many springs ago. Goliath triumphed, and tylluan rolled once, rolled twice, rolled three times under its mass. It was finished.

It tore my heart. I flew into my nest and sobbed.

*

That was the first time I saw Dad cry. There was horror in it, a claustrophobic cavern with a roof touching your head. Father's don't cry.

I returned to Mam.

Dad knelt down on the roadside and carefully picked the injured bird up in his hands. His cheeks were wet as he brought him down from the road.

*

'The bird's alive son! He's alive but very weak!'

I loved that owl. I rolled the stones of my hands across my eyes. I died with him, even though he was breathing.

I remember walking away from the Church and looking back at the barn owl. She seemed so still and strange. Her distance amplified the soundless fear she drew in me...

My parents saved the owl. They gave him some food and carefully placed him in a basket. We were in a car and it wasn't even night time. It was just an owl in the middle of our car. Mam clicked her indicator as we neared the sanctuary.

*

Some years went by, and I was walking in the hills around Soar. I asked my aging father whether an owl actually lived in the church or was it just my childish imagination. He said he remembered something about an owl.

We opened the weathered gate and slipped on the mossy pavement. The congregations of the past watched as we approached the entrance.

I opened the door. The cold air hit me. The pews were fast asleep and the pulpit was as empty as the Judean tomb.

The Duke of Edinburgh boys must have camped there the night before. The old candleholders had sweetie wrappers stuffed into them like ornamental flowers. There were crumbs on the floor and somebody had left their coat.

I couldn't see her and I was devastated.

*

I took the bins out that night.

Suddenly, I remembered the sad episode about the owl.

The moon was given. The night spoke through its light and the gothic trees adorned the blue garments of the sky. Some mice startled as I grabbed the black bags. Slowly I walked with my burden towards the place where the owl was stricken.

Suddenly,
white flashes swept me
unawares. I jumped.
I looked around.
I realised that the flapping was a resurrection.

Grug Muse

Pathetic Fallacy

Rainclouds break their two-week fast
and send a hungry storm
of raindrops – iron-clawed
and raven beaked – to fall
on window panes and tilted roofs.

Thunder
splits the sky like slabs of slate,
grey and green and lilac;
pausing

for effect,
and eating up the lily-scented
white-glove covered
pitter-patter silence

*

They close the curtains for the wake,
to keep the dignified humidity
of the thick and sticky air.

His head lies horizontal –
all unfamiliar lines and angles,
nose pointing up like mast and sail,
rising from that big black ship
that will take him back.
Back, back, back

to the black, black, black
wet earth
where we planted hostas
on hot days, dirt clinging
to the cracks on his hands,
moist and cool.

In church, the clean,
starched light from neon bulbs
gleams smartly on the plastic keys.
They stand to order,
poised and ready
to Ave Maria his soul into the clouds.

I watch a spider, small
on pencil tip toes
climb over hymn sheets
and hang,
suspended
from the seat back
on a single breath of string
ready to fall.

Between Cwm Croesor and Cwmorthin

Perched like sparrows
on a lip of rock
above Cwm Croesor and Cwmorthin.

Up the pass
on an upland of rusted barbs
and slate and crows;
where the carcasses of sheep
rot, unseen between
rush and gorse, in peaty,
ochre streams.

Perched, we watch below
as sunlight spills, like cider
from a tilted cup, and stream
sticky, sweet,
in rivulets along the dry stone walls,
pooling by the farmhouse doors
and running down dirt tracks
towards the sea.

And I am there alone
with you,
just below the clouds.
We tiptoe
through each other's thoughts,
a breadcrumb trail of presence
picked at by the pigeons of our minds.

Peripheral, in my gaze,
slipping through a misty gauze
and sunset haze
on the pass above Cwm Croesor and Cwmorthin.

And so the copper-mittened mountains,
breath held all day,
begin to sigh. Exhale,
slip off their starched
and collared shirts
and whalebone stays.
Relaxed, their muscles soften,
draw us in. Enfold us in their musky night.

And we are perched like sparrows,
asleep, between
Cwm Croesor
and Cwmorthin.

Leanne Nulty

What a state the state is in

We will
always flee and fly away
and escape to another place. We
can trace a deep-rooted compulsion
to leave back through centuries in this
country so consistently defined by a collective
need to grieve. We are so frequently
perceived to be ever-so happy, lucky, and
charming. But that doesn't seem justified
to me when we've been harming generations at an alarming
rate. What a state the state is in when we re-discover the
broken bodies of babies hidden and buried beneath
our soil, when our boys and girls are met with turmoil
at the hands of those who'll exploit them. Stripped of
their voices, their ability to make choices, Well, y'see,
Home Rule meant Rome Rule and it doesn't take much
to stop and reflect, inspect the effects of this heritage
of neglect. We see the state the state is in when
the church fucks us and rights are sin. What
a state the state is in when victims fight but still
can't win. A cacophony of men in suits condoned
this abuse, making excuse after excuse as to why
they refuse to hear us. Perhaps we're too liberal, too
naïve and millennial. Or maybe they just fear us.
Afraid that we reveal the marks that stretch through
this island. Too politically engaged and enraged and too
tired of those who'll try to conceal the deceased. The
very least we ask for is answers. But all I
see is two men: a politician next to a
priest, while I wish they did,
they've not yet brought
us peace

Joseph O'Hagan

Baked Beans

On Monday, Pablo opened a can of baked beans and found four baby carrots hiding in the juice. He hit the orange button which removed the faulty batch from the production line. At the time, he thought that it would be the most exciting thing to happen all week. He felt the same on Tuesday when he pulled the brown lever, watched another can slip down the chute and onto the table in front of him, cut it open, and found it full of baked beans. He hit the green button and the rest of the batch was shipped off to the supermarkets. When the work day was over, Pablo went home with a sack of dented tomato soups which he ate while watching the evening news. He fed his cat, Rodrigo, and went to bed. Wednesday had almost been exciting when he put his apron on back to front, with the label pointing away from his chest, but he noticed and corrected this before he had finished tying the strings behind his back. The can was full of beans, the batch was shipped away, and there weren't any dented soups.

Pablo pulled the brown lever on Thursday and watched the can slip down the chute and onto the table in front of him. He cut it open and found that it wasn't full of baked beans. There was a darkness: black, with whirls of pink and yellow. But brighter. Fuchsias and canaries, yet stronger still. And there were bolts of a Christmas blue, swimming like silk threads through a breeze littered with distant paper lanterns at Chinese New Year. They pulsed and hummed with a deep quietness, yet Pablo swore that they were louder than anything he had previously heard. He poked the surface of the colourful blackness and it rippled under his fingertip, continuing long after he had pulled away. He touched it again, this time plunging his finger deep inside. It was cold. And it was clean. And Pablo thought that it was thin but, when he pulled out his finger, he found that it had clung to his skin and dyed him with a litter of glittering druzy. For the first time in his life, Pablo hit the red button and the conveyor belt crunched to a halt. Alarms fired up an immediate wail through the factory and everyone dropped their jobs in a panic. By the time the foreman had arrived at the quality control station, Pablo had taken the can and run.

Doctor Mills was an old friend that worked at the university. He lifted the can of blackness and read the list of ingredients printed on the back but they gave no explanation. He asked Pablo if they were the same ingredients found in a regular can of beans. Pablo said that they were. Doctor Mills was a biology professor and the smartest man that Pablo knew. Had Pablo been as familiar with physics lecturer Doctor Francis or chemistry lecturer Doctor Andrews as he was with Mills, he would have consulted them instead. Mills poked the blackness with various instruments, took samples and added various chemicals, heated it to coax out a reaction, but none of this produced any kind of result. Ultimately stumped, Doctor Mills shrugged his shoulders and returned the can to Pablo.

Pablo had spent the last of his change on the train to the university and had no choice but to get home by foot. It was difficult to dodge the dense swarms of pedestrians that moved so briskly down the street and Pablo could feel the cold blackness lapping against his palm. He tried to keep the can sealed but the jagged edge of the metal bit into his skin sharply and he pulled his hand back. Some blackness spilled onto the pavement, breaking into a collection of droplets of varying sizes which rolled across the surface of the concrete. Luckily, Pablo managed to catch each drop with the can as they tumbled over the curb. When he looked up he saw a green balloon hanging in the air, rooted to the ground by a small girl with a bowl haircut. She was gawking at him and his mysterious can of beans. No one else was watching, so he let her peek inside. Gently, soft as a breeze, he gave the can a swirl and the small girl watched the colours dance a waltz in the blackness. Fires awoke behind her eyes and she reached for the can, but her mother called out for her. Hush. Pablo put his finger to his lips and got to his feet as the mother arrived to take her daughter away.

Rodrigo had become a creature of habit. On Monday, he watched the pigeons out of the bedroom window. Afterwards, he moved on to scratch the side of Pablo's armchair, then chase the mouse that lived beneath the fridge around the flat until it was time to fall asleep under the coffee table. Pablo found him there after work and prepared dinner. This was repeated on Tuesday *and* Wednesday. So, on Thursday, when Pablo came home during chase time, Rodrigo was uneasy. Pablo didn't notice the mouse disappear beneath the fridge when he put the can of neon blackness on the counter. He thought that maybe he could learn something about his discovery if he poured it out into another container, but his thoughts were interrupted by Rodrigo's incessant mowling. He filled the cat's bowl with Wiskers (an off-brand dusty substitute) while Rodrigo investigated the mysterious object on the side. He sniffed the blackness, patted at it with his paws, and when Pablo turned around, he saw Rodrigo's hind legs disappearing into the can.

Immediately, Pablo sunk his entire arm into the blackness and frantically reached around in all directions, but he could not feel Rodrigo. He pulled out his freshly bedazzled arm and ran for the bedroom. The bedsheet went around his waist, which was intertwined with the wire of his desk lamp. The desk lamp was tied to the left sleeve of his best shirt, while the right connected with a deftly fashioned daisy chain of socks and underwear. Anything with a fraction of flexibility was added to the great rope, which culminated in a roll of cling film gripping to the knob of the one undamaged bedpost. Using tin foil and rubber bands, Pablo fashioned a diving suit, with a helmet made of a clear plastic bowl and tea towels to hold it in place. For his hands, Pablo was lucky enough to have burnt them on the grill the month before, so he had a fresh pair of oven gloves to protect him from the contents of the can. He had nothing for his feet, though, so he hoped that an extra pair of socks and his favourite slippers would be enough. He dipped both arms into the can. He could still feel the gentle cold, but there was no going back now. He dived in head first.

Pablo's eyes did not immediately adjust. His oven gloves thumped the plastic bowl when he attempted to rub them, so he could only squeeze them tightly shut until he was brave enough to look. One eye opened slowly, and when it saw the view, the other followed in amazement. He was floating high among the luminous clouds and rolling stars of the cosmos. A lemon-lime fog crackled with fire in the distance, above a cascading river of amethysts and rubies that circled a planet of the purest gold that Pablo had ever seen, or challenged himself to imagine. He watched a shower of whitest meteoroids pass a solemn moon lost on the horizon when he was spun around by a passing comet with an icy glow that seemed to cool the already chill air, or lack thereof. He watched it tumble faster toward a constellation of blood-orange stars when he noticed that it passed by a small brownish speck in the distance. It was Rodrigo.

Not only did the oven gloves provide Pablo with a degree of warmth that he would not have had otherwise, they also aided him with his breaststroke. In the great expanse of the universe his position did not seem to change, but space glided past him by the mile with every soft brush of his hands. Before long, Rodrigo had grown from a solitary tabby nugget in the emptiness to a kitten stuck in a tree at the end of the road. When he was no more than twenty strokes away, a light appeared in the corner of Pablo's eye. It grew, and it grew again, fast and faster until Pablo turned to see the crown of a glorious sun rising from behind a planet of milk and mint. The void became warm as the raging king of space filled the blackness with an inescapable shine. Raising a glove to cover his eyes in shadow and swimming on with one hand was all Pablo could do to escape his imminent blindness. It was hot now, and Pablo's own breath clouded the inside of his helmet. Rodrigo was panicking too, but saw Pablo fast-approaching and scrambled into his owner's arms.

Only the tail of the sun remained behind the planet and the intense heat began to soften the plastic bowl that shielded Pablo's face. He balled Rodrigo up into his armpit and pulled himself up the Rapunzel's hair of clothes and kitchen accessories. Sweat coated Pablo's hand with a thin slick which sent a glove spiralling off into the vacuum where it burned up in a cluster of hungry flames. Pablo could see a plastic spatula bending at the neck, thinning out the connection between a set of misshapen coat hangers and the old scarf sent to him by his mother for his twenty-sixth birthday. He considered hurling his cat towards the rear end of the tin can that stood at the edge of space and simply allowing the warmth of the galaxy to envelop him in his final moments. But, his fate was spared by a passing storm of intergalactic sleet. It enveloped him, his cat, and his makeshift rope, cooling the perishable links in the chain. Pablo launched himself towards the can of baked beans, approaching with incredible speed. He passed through like a bullet through the barrel of a gun, but when he arrived back in his kitchen, he tumbled gracelessly onto the floor. The mouse had been daring enough to eat Rodrigo's cat food in their absence. Rodrigo leapt from Pablo's arms and chased the creature around the flat while Pablo sat wide-eyed, swallowing breaths like they were of limited supply and in high demand.

Rhea Seren Phillips

The Water Spider

Pull the comfort blanket of obscurity tight;
anesthetise the flesh as setules descend.
There's a consciousness lurking round this parasite.

Walk the path of fog with a stumble to ignite
a deeper book of breath which must only transcend.
Pull the comfort blanket of obscurity tight;

wrench perception through a besotted neophyte.
Weeds entangle an abject mess; wait, suspend;
there's a consciousness lurking round this parasite.

Beads of sweated candle wax shine like anthracite.
Skewer the stakes, there's more than your life to defend.
Pull the comfort blanket of obscurity tight;

I choose banality and weaved stars watertight;
distil leukocytes, watch reality bend.
There's a consciousness lurking round this parasite.

Constrict silver in splinters of meteorite,
dear one hurry, there's a funeral to attend.
Pull the comfort blanket of obscurity tight;
there's a consciousness lurking round this parasite.

The Creamed Cat Gorged on the Curd of the Gallbladder

Feathered claws clink on the linoleum like glass slippers;
curds of bile flourish the floor and scintillates in the sun.
The reservoir is chalked up with sinuous stones that leave
the depths of the old mine it came from fractured and
rimed with
crenelated arteries that blow breath towards the spine.

Mouse languishes on the liver in protest of the distended
stomachs of family, idling on the cranium,
panting for breath as cinders will make his cause redundant.

Morgan Soused the Sodium within the Muscles

An omniscient voice bellowed from the scud of obscurity.
Pinched, *Morgan* drank in the message through mutinous
gills,
saw the shadows of paper boats emerge from the pother
and swam up to greet *the rickety old things* that had
soldered

iron to themselves like starfish. They broke under their
battle cry.
She whispered to the caustic wind that overwhelmed them.
A smile thick as cream made them into tin-pot diving bells
as the archaic language oxidises *them* like salt.

Jack Rendell

Socialising

I went for a coffee with one of my poems.
It had a latte, and I had tea.
'Rhythms of breathing are gorgeous,' it said.
Thank you for writing me.'

'No, no,' I said. 'You don't understand—
Thank *you* for hiding my face!'
Trailing its dactyls in cinnamon foam,
it lathered its grin on the place.

There wasn't an awful lot else to say.
It drained its dregs and rose to leave
I opened my mouth to say something else,
but it always spoke better than me.

Raise my Remains

Take the hollow of my body.
Crack my ribcage like a nut.
Bare my organs to the firelight.
Seek the soul within my gut.

Submerge my heart in blood and grass.
Pack the fleshy valves with earth.
Let me seep into the soil.
Stitch my skin to mossy turf.

Throw my thoughts to heady smoke.
Place my brain in the fire's core.
A lifetime's mental processes
will billow from the forest floor.

Entomb the ashes of my face
among the roots of willow trees.
Then praise the pain-red setting sun
until my eyes are in their leaves.

Brim my lungs with river water.
Rinse until the flow runs clear.
Drape my silk-thin severed wings,
on the pebbles gathered near.

Sink my final earthly pieces
in the trinkling forest blue.
Whisper me throughout the world.
Then I will live anew.

Lands Beyond Green

Find me the creatures in lands beyond green:
honey-kissed mountains and Morrigan moors.
Let's feed the sphinxes on riddlesome fish
and climb with the ogres to platinum tors.

Search out the sea serpent rolling the waves
with a silvery girth that could swallow the sun.
Bring me a water elf straight from the stream.
Tickle it, gurgling, small as your thumb.

Show me the eyes of the dragons that sing.
Symphonies swirl in the clouds of their whites.
The pupils are burning boleros and nocturnes,
watching their notes vibrate valleys and heights.

Take me to people with faces on torsos,
brains in their hearts and their lungs in their throats.
Lead me to tree trolls whose emerald crowns
lurch through the forest like rovering boats.

Crack out the ice-fairies under the Arctic.
Melt out their faces with tea from a flask.
Let's tempt the dryads with gingerbread muffins;
(the ruby-dwarf fathers will bake, if we ask).

Come with me, darling, to worlds beyond wisdom.
Let's go adopt all the creatures we find
on dream-dissolved islands and tropaway realms,
far in the soul-catching heights of your mind.

Gareth Smith

Lost

The little elf, his face twisted in a grimace, turns to watch us. Jacob hurries past, unblinking eyes fixed ahead.

The dummy, roughly the size of Jacob himself, repeats this turning motion in the opposite direction. His sallow face – the colour of sandpaper – has the gurning and rubbery appearance beloved of children's illustrators, but rarely of children themselves. I remember seeing similar elves, likely the exact same ones, adorning grottos and sleighs in supermarkets and department stores throughout my childhood. Perhaps they're almost indestructible, disintegrating as slowly and inconveniently as plastic bags.

This one wears a green outfit fringed with red at the collar, cuffs and ankles. A diamond pattern encircles his waist and the pointed hat perched jauntily atop his straw-like hair. Two hands, looking as though they've been carved from soap, clutch a sign which reads: 'Santa's Grotto – This Way!'.

I wonder whether they switch him off at night. Does his head swivel twenty-four hours a day? I picture him in complete darkness, complete silence, observing this ritual until the sun rises again.

'I can't see it yet, Mam!'

Jacob's hand, within a Minion-shaped mitten, is enveloped in mine. His trainers clap excitedly, cantering against the floor. We walk on the bare ground, over lit strip of linoleum between the car park and the shopping centre. It's an airless corridor, splattered with gum and smelling faintly of urine. I remember dragging my own parents along it, pulling at their sleeves to get to Santa.

He surges ahead, taking us closer to the noise and the lights and the people. He's the only thing propelling me onwards. f he stopped, for whatever reason and if only for a moment, I know I wouldn't take another step. I'm not sure I'd necessarily turn around either, which seems like a different kind of effort. I'd probably just stand exactly where I am, staring emptily at the walls until somebody asked me if everything was alright.

Where would I start with a question like that?

Before I'm even aware of it, the sterile corridor has fallen away and we've emerged into the centre of the centre. It's like stepping inside a wasp's nest. There's buzz and motion all around us, people weaving and bobbing as though practising an unfamiliar dance routine. I can hear Christmas music from multiple unseen speakers. They compete with songs pumping from individual stores, garbling and swilling the tunes into nonsense.

As I'm led beneath tinsel boughs and neon icicles, that feeling, a barely perceptible prickle, is somewhere along my spine. I try and force expressions that I don't feel, reminding myself for the umpteenth time that happy people tend to look happy.

Jacob glimpses something in the distance. He stops abruptly, turning around to gauge my reaction.

In the courtyard of the shopping centre is Father Christmas's grotto. I feel like I'm looking at it from the wrong end of a telescope. I squint to see the snow-peaked roof, the latticed windows and candy-cane picket fence.

I keep my head down as we walk. Focusing on the floor reminds me what an awful colour it is. It looks like they've laminated bile and laid it end-to-end. I occasionally feel it stick to the back of my shoes.

The closer we get to the grotto, the further the illusion is ruined. The snow topped roof is cotton wool; the candy cane fence is peeling and broken. There are other elves scattered around the clapboard house and along the fence, each baring the same expression as their kin at the entrance. Where are these hideous creatures manufactured? Is there one factory that makes them all, plucking each one from a conveyor belt and delivering them all across the world to fulfil their destiny as Christmas gargoyles?

A bored teenager, with felt elf ears on a hairband, is holding a sign that says *Queue Here for Santa* in fancy calligraphy. Behind her are a dozen parents and children waiting anxiously.

Actually, that's a little bit misleading. They're not waiting anxiously. *I am.*

It feels sudden and gradual at once. The room inflates, colour draining out of it like blood. Everything feels slightly off-kilter: perspective is funhouse-mirror warped. I try concentrating on Jacob, honing in on him in my crosshairs, but even he starts to feel less real. It's like I'm watching a video recording of the whole thing.

'Is he inside?'

I shouldn't have done this. I shouldn't. When I suggested taking him today, I'd been given a 'look'. A fleeting, embarrassed 'Are you sure?' glance that had infuriated me.

Of course I was sure. I wasn't the type of person that had to be 'sure' about something so mundane and simple. Otherwise, what type of person would that make me? I could take my son to see Father Christmas. Of course I could. It's what people do.

I'm being led to the end of the queue as though it's the line for the gallows.

There are shop doors all around us. Opening and closing. Swallowing people and regurgitating them. The whole room has slipped from its axis. When I reach my hand out to touch Jacob's head it lands a few inches to the right.

Jacob's chatting. So excited and so very unaware. I know that I'm letting him down. I'm not being what he deserves. I'm not being normal.

I know normal isn't real. Everybody knows that. That doesn't mean it doesn't exist. If you repeat normal often enough, a prayer chanted under your breath, then it becomes as real as anything can be. We're all praying for normal and hoping desperately to remember the words.

I take a gulp of hot air. It barely fills my throat. I take another. Jacob's frantic chatter and gestures have become unintelligible. It's like we're speaking different languages now. I feel my temper rise, my patience sharpen, at the thought that he's doing this on purpose. A flush of guilt follows.

'I don't... I don't think we're going to see him today,' I say it, immensely relieved and equally ashamed. His face, smiles and bright eyes only seconds before, clouds.

'Why?'

'Because...' I see the little girl in front watching us, listening in. I'm jumping for the right words and failing to catch them. 'Because I think that... we don't have...'

His lips draw slowly together. His eyes narrow. I've seen this before. Tears are seconds away.

Oh God. Oh No. Oh Shit.

I turn quickly away from him, drawing a shuddering breath from the depths of my lungs. I look around at the rest of the shoppers. My vision blurs and clears like a camera adjusting focus. I can't tell the noises in the crowd from the songs in the speaker anymore.

I've made up my mind. I'll go home. I'll tell them the truth. Or I'll lie. Whatever. It doesn't matter. What matters is that I leave.

I turn back.

Jacob's gone.

He's not where he was and he's not nearby. I lean to the side, checking that he hasn't idly skipped the queue. The girl with the beady eyes is now chatting away to her mother, oblivious. I complete a slow, three hundred and sixty degree turn to make sure that he's not standing behind me.

What's surprising is that, for the first time since I awoke this morning, I don't feel gripped by dread. It's like a numbing agent has been applied to my nerves. I feel strangely empty as I stand alone in the queue, searching for my missing son.

I calmly step sideways, as though that had been my intention all along, and casually circumnavigate the grotto. I keep waiting to see him climbing on the candy cane fences but it's empty at every turn. As I pass the exit, a door opens and a small family emerge. The toddlers, twin girls in matching purple raincoats, wave frantically at Santa before the door closes again.

I've come full circle and he's still gone.

I'm keeping a lid on my calm, pushing down my emotions that rise at the back of my throat like fresh, warm bile. My eyes drift, back and forth, back and forth, waiting for the moment where I see him and this whole horrific episode evaporates. I'm imagining the relief before it's happened.

I wonder if it's noticeable that something's wrong. Has anyone realised that the woman with the little boy is now standing alone?

Maybe they all have. Perhaps they're all covertly watching me, eyes drifting evasively away whenever I try to catch them out. I imagine that every head in the building is turning to look at me. It happens slowly and effortlessly and with the same mechanical motion as the elves. A new pair of eyes every few seconds, clustered together like a spider's.

They're waiting to see what I'll do next. They're waiting for the moment where I scream for help and admit my defeat. They want me to shout my name – loud and clear – across the centre so that everybody knows exactly what to call me. I picture newspaper headlines, reports on the television and angry Facebook rants.

I jolt my head suddenly, trying to trap a watcher, but nobody's looking in my direction. I'm just scaring myself, as usual.I do that sometimes. It's like I'm trying to push myself to imagine something truly, irreversibly, awful and prove to myself that I'm as far gone as I think.

At a distance, I can see a portly middle-aged man in a yellow visibility jacket. I could do the sensible thing and report Jacob's disappearance to him. That's what any other parent would do in this situation.

That's exactly what a *normal* parent would do in this situation.

I reach a shaking hand in my pocket and take my mobile phone out. I pretend to read something, staring only at my shadowed reflection on the screen. I nod decisively, returning the phone to my pocket, and walk purposefully away from the grotto.

*

Maybe I never had a son. Perhaps Jacob was a delusion. Stranger things have happened. I might've created him as I was getting out of the car, weaving a backstory that went all the way back to the day he was born. When I got distracted, he vanished into the air from whence he came.

Stop – doing it again. Scaring myself.

I've been in this café for ten minutes. It's built like a conservatory in the corner of the Centre, allowing me to feel like a goldfish within two bowls. I ordered a cup of coffee, and inexplicably, a slice of carrot cake. I've been here since, staring at the other customers and eating pinches of the cake.

An old lady, replete with colourless Mackintosh and matching trolley, is sat close to the counter. Every movement she makes looks like an effort. Three teenagers are trying to connect to the Wi-Fi, continually shouting at the staff to repeat the password. A mother with two boys is watching them eat ham rolls, a glazed look in her eyes.

Will they interview them, I wonder? When the 'story' breaks and everybody knows what I've done, will they appeal to other diners for first impressions? They'll definitely approach the staff. A middle-aged woman with dirty blonde hair in an unravelling bun took my order. There's a teenage girl working the coffee machine and periodically checking her phone when she thinks no-one's looking.

'*She didn't say much really...*' I'm imagining her voice even though I've never heard it. '*Just ate her cake and sat there. She didn't look funny, but they never do, do they?*'

With every second that I've stayed here, I've dug

another handful of dirt from my grave. It's going to be one thing to explain that I lost Jacob. It's going to be another to explain why I calmly walked away from the situation and went for a bite to eat. It's going to sound – it's going to sound... don't say it.

Crazy.

Oh, you've done it now.The word you've been running away has found you. There's no need to think in hypotheticals any more – the *what ifs* and the *might ifs* are gone now. You've got a tangible example of insanity that people can shackle you to.

Did you hear about what she did? Yes, she lost him. But after that – did you hear what she did after that? Yes, I'm serious. I know! I know! It's *crazy*.

I've been tapping my fingers on the table, moving rhythmically from little finger to thumb without even realising it. The tips are sticking slightly to the surface of lemon-scented disinfectant.

What do I now? What the hell am I supposed to do?

Jacob's walking towards me. His face is a choked pink and his eyes are bloodshot. A wet hand points in my direction. A woman in black, hair and make-up perfectly styled, is holding his other hand.

I don't really have time to process the shock, surprise or relief. I only have time to remember what I need to do in this situation. It comes naturally to me because it has to.

I take a sudden, chest opening breath, and with it I change my demeanour completely. I stand, my face blossoming into gratitude and relief. I open my arms towards Jacob, running towards him. He's smiling by the time I've reached him and I scoop him up as though we'd rehearsed the whole routine. I can feel his warm face against my hair and hear his teary giggles echo in my ear.

I turn to the woman, Jacob's face buried in my shoulder. 'Thank you so much. I was just about to call the police.'

There's a second when I worry she's going to question me. She could so easily raise an eyebrow and ask what I was doing sat in the café. It would be the first in a slew of accusations. Instead, she smiles.

'No problem.We found him crying by the doors. Poor dab. You alright now?'

Jacob turns his head, nodding enthusiastically.

'I've been worried sick,' I lie. 'I just turned around and he was gone. I've been everywhere.'

'Happens to everyone at some point,' the woman replies. 'I'd best get back.'

She gives Jacob a squeeze on the arm. I thank her once again. She begins walking away and disappears into the crowd.

'It's okay, Jacob. No need to cry.'

I give him another cwtch and then, very delicately, place him back onto the floor.

'Shall we go home then?'

He nods. He's already forgotten about Santa.

'Don't worry... Mam's here now...'

Who's that meant to comfort? I take his hand again.

Together, we walk back into the crowds and underneath the decorations. We walk through the narrow alleyway and towards the car park. Although I make a concerted effort not to see for myself, I know that the little elf watches us leave and then turns his head away.

Thomas Tyrrell

Three Wimbledon sonnets
or
Serve, return and rally

The world eyes now each young Adonis,
Achilles or Endymion
Who vies to triumph in the tennis
On centre court at Wimbledon.
White spotless shorts and skirts are gleaming;
On Henman Hill the crowds are teeming
To view the game of skill and nerve:
The hundred-mile-an-hour serve,
Forehand, backhand, return and rally,
Lobs, slices, double-faults and aces
To put the players through their paces,
As points and sets mount on the tally:
The challenge, and the awful doubt—
Was the ball in? Or was it out?

To rhyme on people's names is tacky
But hard to shun, when you can switch
From Williams v. Wozniacki
To Federer v. Djokovic.
Writing free verse would be a let-down
Like playing tennis with the net down.
(I stole that line from Robert Frost.)
Played badly, all the tension's lost;

Played well, and golf has nothing on it.
To one enraptured as I am,
A point can be an epigram,
Or make an interweaving sonnet
Where human talent awes and shines
Enclosed in arbitrary lines.

My talent? No, I wholly lack it;
I drove my tutors to despair.
I hardly know to hold a racquet
Or throw a ball into the air.
My mother thought my imperfection
Might be improved by close direction.
She schooled me in my stance and pose,
I swung – and hit my mother's nose.
(It's quite the painful family story.)
And from that day, I've had no thought
Of shining on a tennis court.
Let others dream of sporting glory,
Trophies, applauding crowds. I dream
Of court-side seats, and strawberries, and cream.

Sometimes in Summer

(Second Prize, Poetry)

Sometimes in Summer drifts of thistledown
Blow through as thick as blizzards that would drown
Fields, hills and woods in vegetable snow,
And then the skylark, like an autumn leaf,
Floats down to settle on the open heath
Where no tree is, nor tree will ever grow.

Sometimes at dusk my step disturbs a moth
That flutters up, shook from the somber cloth
That grey-clad Evening lays across the vale,
Or from her heather bed a partridge springs,
Scurrying skyward in a whirr of wings,
To flee my heavy tramp along the trail.

And sometimes in the waning of the year,
The air lies crisp and still, the light falls clear,
After a day of bluster, gust, and squall,
While in its final blaze of gold and red
A dead leaf dangles by a spider's thread,
Precariously suspended in its fall.

Emma Varney

The Silence of Smartphone

The clock didn't tick anymore
It lit up at intervals
Between the takeaway deals
The game requests
And the likes of that photo
I took twenty-five times

Because my smile wasn't right

The passing of time was measured
By the Instagram feed
Which showed me how much
Of my life I wasn't living
Compared to everyone else

With filters

Water

Each day I break
A roaring wave
I break and remake
Coming back together
Stronger than before

And I'll keep breaking
And remaking
Until I reach the shore

Holly Venus

After a Poet Leaves

The wind doesn't talk here
without you.
It staggers about the farm, drunk
with wishing, and moans in the bathtub
drain. Life moves slower now,
I'm sure.
Moelfre is a shape
in the dark, where the sun
has forgotten to laugh – a blunted point
someone never tried to make.
It watches me
as I hop the stony skeleton of a valley
bent by your words.
I haven't been inside the house
but its hinges creak soft
poetry like you.
Little else is spoken through the stone,
though a fire lights its windows,
and the smoke draws
a new face on the moon.

A House Forgets

Old photo frames, fractured
china ornaments,
and forgotten
pairs of reading
glasses line the shelves
of a solid home chiselled
by the deep valley air.
Matching coats, hats,
scarves scatter
the sanctuary of the porch.
Compass by the front door,
backpack hanging
heavy on the last hook. Gloveless,
pen and notebook in hand,
you stand,
ready to consume Cwm Nantcol
in its rocky bed.
But when you leave,
your objects leave
with you. The stories loosen
until your favourite armchair becomes
just a piece of furniture.
The house remembers
only itself, and the empty space
you once occupied.
It cannot keep us safe
from time

taking,
or bricks that slip
our image through the cement
and into a valley
that will learn to forget us too.

Josh Weeks

Llanederyn to Las Ventas

The horn had entered just above the right thigh.

'It's bad', said the doctor, directing his words to one of the picadors. 'The wound is deep. He's bleeding out fast.'

The doctor passed a sheet of gauze around his midriff and secured it using his cape, but the sand beneath him was already gummy with blood; his face grown cold in the midday heat.

'He needs surgery if he's going to live – it can't wait, it has to be this instant.'

The doctor searched through his bag of instruments with a calmness that seemed inhuman. When he removed a scalpel and a ball of thread, the *picador* joined the others in trying to tame the bull. Its nostrils were flared and its eyes were aflame, filled with a fury that only death can temper. It charged across the arena leaving hoof prints in its trail, which the guards were smoothing over, ready for the next fight.

'You need to focus', he heard the doctor say. 'I need you to focus on something – a face, a cloud, anything – just don't close your eyes.'

He looked down and saw a circle of red growing gradually bigger, like an apocalyptic sun. He looked up at the stands, searching for his mother and father. He couldn't see them anywhere. His eyes were beginning to slide under their lids.

He'd heard that Joselito went out the same way. One final flourish for the crowd; a slip to the left him too close to the bull. He wondered if he regretted it – the mistake that finished him at the peak of his career. Was this the pass that made him? Was his death a secret relief?

He felt at the sequins of his traje de luces; smoothed his fingers over the gold and silver thread that fastened the seams between torso and shoulders. He heard the crowd roaring. They were chanting his name: viva el matador! Was this the perfect end?

His name was Matthew. Matt, for short. But to those who saw him roaming Cardiff city centre on a Saturday morning, his name was Matador.

Christie, the burger man, had always been one to plague him: 'I haven't got any bull but I can do you a bit of bacon...?'

Sometimes it was the valleys boys who'd travelled down for the game, tearing their shirts from pumped up torsos and flaring them outwards like outlet-store capes. There was an occasion when he charged at a Ben Sherman-shaped target, momentarily becoming the beast he sought to provoke. He returned home with a bloody nose and a patch of sequins missing from his jacket, the sound of laughter still ringing in his ears.

'For Christ's sake!' his father yelled.'Can't you get into football and girls like every other lad your age?'

'Leave him alone, Dai. Being a teenager's difficult these days – he's still finding his feet.'

His father slammed his copy of the *Daily Mail* down on the kitchen counter.

'Finding his feet? He's been banging on about bastard

Las Ventas since he was seven years old! The boy's obsessed, Love. He needs to be told.'

He looked at his mother, the way her spine curved; the streaks of grey hair that caught in her wrinkles as she stood over the sink, looking for something to wash up. When he was young he couldn't imagine her ever looking old. Now, he could only hope he wasn't the one to blame for it.

He could still remember it clear as day: that early morning start; the sun beating down as they were led by a tour guide through the winding streets of Madrid.

When he first saw Las Ventas he thought it was a football stadium. He'd yet to be dragged along to Ninian Park to watch the Bluebirds play, and given the fervour with which his father spoke about the team, this grand sandstone circle of columns and vaults was not dissimilar to the image he had in his mind. But when they entered through the giant red doors, and he saw the ring of sand where a matador was practising, it was as if all the things he'd been taught to appreciate had suddenly crumbled to dust, and all that was left was him and the matador, standing at the centre of the universe.

'Look,' he pointed. 'Look at him dancing!' The matador was holding out a red cape – his body swivelling on an invisible axis as he snatched it away like the remnants of a dream. His suit was covered in what looked like diamonds, and his hair – jet black and impossibly shiny – seemed to be moulded to his head with licks of paint. His parents wanted to go for lunch but he wasn't having any of it. 'Please! Just let him finish the dance first – the tour hasn't finished and I'm not even hungry.'

They stayed to watch the matador, and the guide told them all about the legendary Joselito – how he was the greatest bull fighter that ever lived; how his death made the whole country come to a standstill in like no other tragedy before or since. Eventually he ran out of things to say and asked if there were any questions. His hand moved quicker than the matador's cape. 'How do you become a matador?' he asked, struggling for breath.

The next few weeks all he talked about was Las Ventas. He begged his mother to buy him a traje de luces, and when she asked him what that was, he told her off for not listening during the tour. She managed to find him one somewhere on the Internet – a tattered fancy dress outfit whose spattering of plastic sequins dangled from the fabric; a yellow piss stain circling the crotch. He wore it every day – out to play, to his grandparents' house, even to bed – and when school started back after the summer holidays he was absolutely distraught at having to finally take it off.

'It's just a phase', his parents would say. They spent parents' evening explaining why their son's hair was thick with Brylcreem; why he'd convince his friends to charge at him between the desks as he held out a red book folder, before snatching it above their heads. But before they knew it he was eight years old. Then nine. Then ten. Then fifteen. His early teens passed them like a raging bull, but the only real change was the size of his traje. He used all the money from his paper round to have a custom-made jacket sent from Seville, and his mother was always careful to have a clean pair of her stockings ready in his sock drawer, so that he wouldn't have to ask. In short, they knew that their son was just as strange as ever. Their son was still Matador, and there was seemingly nothing they could do about it.

After his first day of Sixth Form they'd decided to test the waters. They gathered in the living room; his mother poured out cups of tea whilst his father put on his best impression of empathy.

'Look, we know that you're interests are a little left field – but we think it's about time you time you started thinking about your future.'

'My future?' he replied, removing his montera and loosening his necktie. 'How you mean?'

His father glanced at his mother, who busied herself with the biscuit tin. He took a deep breath in leaned forward in his seat. 'I mean your future, Matt. University. A job...'

'I'm not going to university.'

'I'm sorry?'

'I'm moving to Spain – I'm going back to Las Ventas.'

There was a moment of silence as his father sunk back into his seat. It was broken by the rattling of china as his mother handed each of them a cup and saucer.

'Spain?' he said, the façade falling from his face. 'Get a fucking grip will you! You're sixteen years of fucking age and you're still prancing about in your bastard Strictly outfit!'

'Watch your language,' said his mother.'There's no need to be aggressive.'

'Me? Aggressive? Well that's charming. You've got a son who thinks he's a bullfighter and all you care about is my fucking language.'

He got to his feet and made his way towards the door.

'And where do you think you're going? We're not done here – not even close.'

His father was almost shaking; the veins in his forehead threatening to burst through the skin.

'Out to the fields', he answered indifferently. 'You can leave my dinner in the microwave, Mam.'

He shut the door behind him and left his parents

left to argue amongst themselves. He'd heard that the farmer down at Cefyn Madly Park had recently acquired a bull.

'Well I can't bloody believe it', said Christie as he sliced a burger-bun. 'Sixteen years of age – he was only by there a few days ago.' He pointed towards the thoroughfare between his van and House of Fraser; drops of sweat falling onto the grill as he shook his head in disbelief.

He passed the burger over to customer, who rushed away as quickly as he could. He was too in shock to distinguish between those who cared and who didn't.

It was strange, that Saturday morning – the way the city centre seemed hollow in a way, despite the shoppers and rugby fans that crammed the streets. Wales were playing against Ireland in the Six Nations, and though streams of red jerseys made their way to the Millennium, none were as red as the small square of fabric that Christie was used to seeing, wavering in the air like a flame.

The police had informed his parents an hour after it happened. The paramedics had gotten to Cefyn Madley as quickly as they could, but he'd been gored in his lower stomach, and by the time the farmer found him he was already half gone.

For a while they didn't speak – not to each other nor anyone else. His mother kept her mourning to herself, staring at her reflection in the bathroom mirror as she cried, as if doubling her suffering might speed up the process. His father, meanwhile, just sat in his armchair and read all day. At least it looked like he was reading. He often ended up just staring at the pages.

But then one day they had a call from a local journalist. He'd heard about Matt – how he'd become a bit of a celebrity amongst the locals – and wanted to do a story about how he'd come to be known as Matador.

His mother was the one who'd answered the call, and at first she was scared of his father might react. But surprisingly he said yes. He said he thought it could be helpful, in a way, and that evening the journalist came round to the house for an interview.

'Las Ventas, you say? How old was he at the time.'

'Seven', replied his father, 'it was a family holiday to Madrid.'

The journalist nodded and stuffed his thumb into his beard, jotting something down as his mother put a cup of tea in front of him.

'And he was a good boy? Well behaved... or was he sometimes a little unruly?'

'He was different', his father said. 'Not in a bad way, just different.'

The journalist smiled and continued his jotting.

'And his death?'

'What about it?'

'Well, were you shocked? Were you confused?'

His mother gave his father a nervous glance.

His father thought it over for a moment, rubbing the corners of his eyes as if it was only his tiredness that made the answer elude him. 'Just make sure the headline reads exactly as I've told you,' he said, getting to his feet and shaking the journalist's hand. 'There's no worth in dwelling on how we feel about it.'

The following Saturday, just after he'd been the butcher's to pick up some supplies for the Wales vs. Scotland match, Christie popped to the newsstand to get his daily copy of *The Sun*. It was about an hour or so before the punters would begin arriving in droves for their breakfast butties, and he liked to read the back pages before getting bogged down in petty change and bacon grease.

'Looks like Bellamy's heading back to the Bluebirds', said the vendor. 'They say he's got a coaching role with the youth set-up.'

Christie searched in his pocket and handed him a pound. 'It'd make a change, wouldn't it? Seems like all ex-pros nowadays just sit on their arses all day and stare at TV monitors.'

The vendor nodded in agreement and handed him the change. But just as Christie turned to make his way back up towards The Hayes, he saw a copy of *The South Wales Argus* perched on one of the stands.

He grabbed it and stared at the front page in astonishment.

It was him: matador, standing tall and majestic in his sparkling traje. His montera was perched on the crown of his head, and cape was flared outwards, as if inviting the gaze of the viewer to charge onwards into the image. Christie laughed to himself; shaking his head that way people do when the world seems as baseless as the words we use to define it.

Matthew 'Matador' Collins, read the headline, *Dies in Las Ventas, Madrid.*

Daniel Williams

After the Kiss

The Kiss (Lovers), Gustav Klimt, 1908–1909

As the canvas settles
out of sunlight, they reclaim
their lived-in lives in stages
from the line of hooks, remembering
the possibility of strangers, the scent
of pipe smoke, a trace of cologne;

her third-hand gloves flex and straighten
her dress, his jacket is worn thin
at the elbow where he has leant on
his fortune at the card table,
laid out his hand
and lost.
Absently, he holds the door
as she moves first,
close, and props her hat
as though entering a second pose;
he tightens his neck-tie, steps out
into the street and spits.
That evening, when her hat sits
like a relic in its preserved box,
the still-warm gloves stretched
on the chair back,
he tints the air blue

with burnt tobacco,
red gas light draping him in shadow
like a mourner's robe, and only the canvas holds
to the certainty of his grip,
its want and brightness, her face upturned
while behind the tight lids
she records his imprint
like a seismograph, the moment
she re-enters
as the shutters are opened
on Vienna
and the roof slates
blink gold.

The Vanished

The spot they chose bordered the lake. The man and his son pitched their tent, tugging the frame upright and pegging down the guide ropes to the hard earth. The man dwelt on the graininess of the dirt between his fingers, the unfamiliar act of truly using his hands.

When the work was done he led the boy down to the shore. It was still bright. The lake held the whole of the sky like an upturned mirror. The summer had started out harsh and dry, each garden they'd passed on the drive already dull and yellowed with drought.

The boy put his shoes and socks aside and took a few cautious steps into the water. The still numbing cold made him dart back, laughing. The man laughed with him and loosened his toes from his sandals.

Skirting the edge, he looked for a stone to skim, taking time to scout for one that was flat and smooth enough; he had been taught that himself. He tested the weight of each in his palm, drawing back his arm steadily like a bow string – one bounce, another, another... He sent a second in its wake and the boy began to imitate him, testing his own stone like an initiate and giving it his approval. The boy's arced briefly and disappeared with a weighty slap. Their laughter carried through the quiet as the man watched. He'd show the boy how his stones could resist that drop into the dark.

It was as his father straightened up, ready with the next rock, that the boy spotted it.

'Look!' he said, pointing out at the water, the sunlight

glancing towards them.

The man squinted behind his dark glasses and stared. It was a mound like a small, sudden island, tapered to an unnatural point.

As he scrutinised the shape, something swam up at him as from a memory, but not his own, not first-hand. A page patterned with black and white frames, their rough edges preserved. His own father's hands had pointed back into the pictures, smoothed their extent, his blue veins visible like unnamed tributaries. A valley survived beneath the weight of the water, the traces of residents fixed here as firmly as the stone that had built their homes. A cluster of cottages, farm land, a chapel on which to centre each Sunday. They had been removed, despite resistance, been made to disassemble the lives they'd led, could even carry their uninterred dead if they wished, but the land would be wiped clean. The valley was flooded, a reservoir built to power industry to the north, to provide the days to come with a new and different pulse. The man realised what was surfacing as the heat went on.

'What is it?' the boy asked.

'People lived here,' the man answered. 'A long time ago.'

The boy briefly imagined amphibious folk with the slashes of gills across their lean bodies, webbed hands and feet, drifting through their daily lives submerged

The man stayed fixed on the discovery, thought of circling high above it, seeing the farms and squat houses laid out as though under a sheet of glass in a display box, the spire of the chapel reaching up and through it. Nowhere was blank, not entirely.

'Where did they go?'

'I don't know. Maybe where we're going.'

'And where's that?'

'You'll see.'

In truth the man didn't know, though he was certain by now they would be looking for the boy. It could have been simpler than this. Clare's call to the school would unravel. Slowly, half-unbelieving, half-resigned, she would realise what he had done.

He wanted their history to stay permanently out of sight. Finally, he looked away from the peak of the spire. The stone had dried in his palm and become slick again with sweat.

'C'mon,' he said to the boy.

He pulled back, released the stone toward the water and turned for their tent. He didn't wait to hear it vanish.

Timothy Wynne

February

Our fascination
with the moon
began on the 6th day
when the main road
still led past the post-office
and I'd buy
Lambert and Butler's
from the Spar
when I hadn't yet
become obsessed with failure.

I'd rather you
saw me on a good day
when I've shaved
when I fit
into something nice
something I haven't
in a long while

If I'm changing
so be it
but let me be angry about it
and then
let me be sad.

Author Biographies

Thomas Baker is a 28-year-old graduate of Cardiff University, originally from Blaenllechau in the Rhondda but now living in Newport. He has been commended and published in previous *Cheval* anthologies.

Yalan Bao, born and raised in eastern China, is a scholar, poet and short-story writer living in Durham. She holds a B.A. in English literature from Aberystwyth University and is currently completing her M.A in English literary studies at Durham University, where she studies poetry and poetics among other things.

Kathy Chamberlain moved to Swansea in 2011, when she embarked on her postgraduate studies. Her thesis consisted of short stories characterised by isolation and anomalousness, reflecting her interest in all things quirky. She's a big fan of circular narratives and plain style prose. Kathy teaches undergraduate classes in creative writing and English literature.

Emily Cotterill is a Cardiff-based poet originally from Alfreton, Derbyshire. She first moved to Wales in 2010. Emily writes about the sense and meaning of place, she has a day job in the same vein and often wonders why she did not study geography.

Ashleigh Davies is a graduate of Cardiff Metropolitan University. His writing has appeared in *Poetry Wales, New Welsh Review* and *Iota* amongst other publications.

Rhodri Diaz is a writer from Swansea. A first-language Welsh speaker, Rhodri enjoys writing about the wealth of fascinating and occasionally peculiar characters that inhabit Swansea and the valleys beyond. His story 'Beyond You And Me' was published in last year's *Cheval* anthology.

Mari Ellis Dunning is an award-winning Welsh writer of poetry, short stories and children's books. She lives with her husband on the coast of Swansea which is sometimes grey and always glorious. Her debut poetry collection, *Salacia,* will be launching summer 2018 with Parthian. Her favourite things in the world are dogs, chocolate and books.

Emily Hancox studied creative writing at South Wales University. Her first book, *Ballerina* was published three years ago, she often appears in *South Wales Evening Post*, and runs poetry workshops at Aberdulais, National Trust. She is currently working on her new project, 'Postcard Poetry' a collection of poems from her travels.

Kimberley Houlihan currently lives in Bridgend with her partner and young daughter. She completed her MA in creative writing at Swansea University in 2016. Currently, she is working on a collection of short stories and is attempting to complete a rather tricksy first novel.

Niall Ivin writes short stories well in advance of deadlines and is from Risca, South Wales. He was previously commended in the 2015 Robin Reeves Prize, and is hoping to commence an MA in creative writing at Cardiff University in 2018.

Katya Johnson is in the final year of her PhD in creative writing at Aberystwyth University. Her writing explores ways in which human identity is shaped by our environment and creative processes. Katya's critical work and fiction has been published by *New Welsh Review*, *Poetry Wales* and *New Writing*.

Philip Jones is a writer and musician (performing as Dusty Cut) from Pembrokeshire. Runner up in the 2015 People, Place & Planet: WWF Cymru Prize for Writing on Nature and the Environment New Welsh Writing Awards. A Cardiff University creative writing MA graduate and Hay Festival Writer at Work.

Rebecca Lawn is a freelance writer, living in Cardiff. She studied for an MA in creative writing at Cardiff University and has had short stories published in *Cheval 10*, *The Lonely Crowd* and *Litro*, among others.

James Lloyd is a 24-year-old writer living in Gwynedd. He is currently studying creative writing and film studies at Bangor University, with an interest in the landscape, environment and culture. His poems in this anthology are concerned with human impact and what we leave behind when we're gone.

Eddie Matthews is a PhD in creative writing student at Swansea University. His stories explore how borders influence our behaviour. He aims to use storytelling to create space for positive dialogue about the shared human experience.

Eve Elizabeth Moriarty works with virtual reality at Swansea University, where she is also a PhD creative writing candidate. Eve was a winner in the 2015 Robin Reeves Award and received a Literature Wales bursary in 2017 to work on her collection *Radium Girls*. Her poetic interests include feminism, mental health, history and place.

Michael Muia is a first year history & creative writing student at Wrexham's Glyndwr University. He is an army veteran having served with the Welsh Guards in Bosnia and Afghanistan. Michael is currently working on several short stories and has aspirations of writing for the stage. He is father of three small children and enjoys staying active by playing rugby.

Nathan Munday is a final year PhD student at Cardiff and Aberystwyth Universities. He originally comes from Carmarthenshire but now lives in Cardiff. His recent book, *Seven Days: A Pyrenean Adventure* (Parthian: 2017), came second in the New Welsh Travel Writing Awards 2016.

Grug Muse is a (AHRC-CDT in Celtic studies funded) PhD student at the Welsh department at Swansea. She won the chair at the 2013 Urdd eisteddfod; is co-editor of *Y Stamp*; a member of the Cywion Cranogwen collective; and in 2017 published her first volume of poetry, *Ar Ddisberod* with Cyhoeddiadau Barddas.

Leanne Rose Nulty is an Irish poet currently living in Aberystwyth, where she completed a degree in English literature and creative writing. Her poetry covers a range of topics including womanhood, politics, grief, and national identity.

Joseph O'Hagan is an English and creative writing student at Cardiff Metropolitan University. Cardiff has been his home since 2015. Aside from a short story published in his university's *Metropolitan* anthology, Joseph's work has gone largely unpublished, but he hopes of one day publishing his own series of children's books.

Rhea Seren Phillips is a PhD student at Swansea University. She is researching how to reconsider Welsh cultural identity through Welsh poetic forms and metre. Rhea has been published in *Gogoneddus Ych-a-Fi*: an exhibition of work by contemporary Surrealists (2018), *Molly Bloom* (2018), *Cheval 10* (2017) and *The Luxembourg Review* (2017).

Jack Rendell is a poet and fantasy writer pursuing an MA in creative writing. He lives with his fiancée Alice and the family, including a large menagerie of animals. His work has appeared in the *Aberystwyth MA Anthology*, the *Electric Reads Young Writers' Anthology* and in *Cheval 10*.

Gareth Smith is from Neath but currently lives and works in Swansea. He enjoys entering drama and prose competitions both locally and nationally. He had a short play performed for the Sherman Cymru's 40th Anniversary celebrations, was shortlisted for a BBC writing competition and has appeared in several previous *Cheval* anthologies.

Thomas Tyrrell is now a two-time winner of the Terry Hetherington poetry prize. He lives in Cardiff and recently completed a doctoral thesis on John Milton and eighteenth-century poetry at Cardiff University. His work has also appeared in *Lonesome October* and *Words for the Wild*.

Emma Varney loves nothing more than writing day after day and is always bothered when reality barges in. She's open and honest, particularly with her mental health struggles. Emma surrounds herself with bright colours, decent coffee and Biscoff.

Holly Venus was born and raised in Cardiff. She studied a Bachelor's degree in English literature and creative writing in Aberystwyth and went on to complete a Master's degree with a focus on poetry. She has recently returned to Wales after travelling and writing in New Zealand for a year.

Josh Weeks is a writer from Caldicot, South Wales, who is currently studying for a PhD in Latin American literature at the University of Amsterdam. His previous work has been longlisted for the Bath Flash Fiction Award, as well as featuring in *Ellipsis Zine* and *Five 2 One* Magazine.

Daniel Williams is a Cardiff-based writer and editor working in independent publishing. He completed an MA in creative writing at Cardiff University in 2016 and his poetry has been featured by *Envoi*, *Cadaverine* and *Ink, Sweat and Tears*, among others. He is also founding editor of *Long Exposure* magazine.

Timothy Wynne is a third year English and creative writing student at Cardiff Metropolitan University. He enjoys exploring themes of identity in modern Wales and is particularly interested in expressions of queerness and the complexities of domestic relationships.

Acknowledgements

The Terry Hetherington Young Writers Award is in the namesake of my late partner Terry Hetherington who died in 2007, a popular poet and performer.

I am most grateful to the team at the Dylan Thomas Centre, Swansea, who have provided ongoing support and a venue for the awards evenings.

Both Jo Furber and Alan Kellerman, together with Alan Perry, Jean Perry and Amanda Davies were the initial instigators of the award.

I appreciate the dedication of our Trustees: Phil Knight, Amanda Davies, Huw Pudner, Kirsty Parsons, Liza Osborne, Rose Widlake, Glyn Edwards and Jonathan Edwards. Thanks also to our volunteers Kym and Brendan Barker, Whyt Pugh, Michael O'Neill, and Nathan Davies.

Thanks to Parthian Books for their support of the award, expertise and publication of the *Cheval* series. A special appreciation goes to Richard Lewis Davies, Director, for his ongoing interest and support for all the young writers involved with the award, and to Maria Zygogianni for her skills and advice on the format. Thanks to Siôn Tomos Owen for his artistic skills.

It is so rewarding to receive ongoing support from previous winners and commended writers who have become published writers and poets themselves: Jonathan Edwards as a judge and editor, Rose Widlake and Glyn Edwards for editing *Cheval 11*, and the young writers who support the event year after year.

The main source of fundraising is through the

dedication of contributors to Cheval: Neath Poems and Pints, held every month at the Cambrian Arms, Melyn. We are especially grateful to the proprietors Dewi, Gavin and Colin. Other contributors are Neath Town Council Grant Aid, Cambrian Arms Quiz Team and members donations from the Owain Glyndwr Society. Individual donors include Dave and Gwyneth Hughes, the late Nigel Jenkins, Margot Morgan, Jen and Mike Wilson, Gwenda Lloyd, Margaret Webley, Michael Oliver, and Christopher Hyatt.

Thank you to everyone who provides raffle prizes both at Poems and Pints and at the awards evenings, to all individual supporters, Parthian Books, Alun Books (especially Sally Roberts Jones) and Tesco Neath Abbey.

The administration of the Terry Hetherington Young Writers Award is provided by Malcolm Lloyd, who does so much more than provide the website; www.chevalwriters.org.uk. The website is continually updated and contains profiles of young writers, their ongoing progress and their books. There is also an online shop that sells all previous *Cheval* series books, some for sale at low cost. Videos of the awards evenings and Poems and Pints can also be viewed on the website. I am indebted to Malcolm for all his involvement.

Each year, publicity for the Award is provided by Mark Rees of the *South Wales Evening Post*. He attends the awards evenings, and shows genuine interest in the young writers and their progress.

Year after year past friends of the late Terry Hetherington attend the Terry Hetherington Young Writers Awards evenings, purchasing books, buying raffle tickets, and supporting the young writers. The list is too long to mention everyone. Among the friends are;

Amber Hiscott, Liz Hobbs, Steve Croke, Angela Weeks, Sian and Paul Lloyd Jones, Ioan Ap Trefor, Enoch and Iris Richard, Dewi Bowen, Linda and Stan Kinsey, Mike Burrows, Marian Frances, Byron and Sandra Beynon, Humberto and Gabriella Garcia, Gareth and Sheila Pawan.

Cheval is a voluntary organization. Our registration is provided by Neath Port Talbot Voluntary Service and we are most grateful for their help and advice to maintain our voluntary status.

Aida Birch